M337 Unit D2
Mathematics: A Third Level Course

COMPLEX ANALYSIS

UNIT D2 FLUID FLOWS

Prepared by the Course Team

Before working through this text, make sure that you have read the *Course Guide* for M337 Complex Analysis.

The Open University, Walton Hall, Milton Keynes, MK7 6AA.

First published 1993. Reprinted 1995, 1999, 2003, 2006

Edited, designed and typeset by the Open University using the Open University TeX System.

Printed in Malta by Gutenberg Press Limited.

ISBN 0 7492 2187 9

This text forms part of an Open University Third Level Course. If you would like a copy of *Studying with The Open University*, please write to the Central Enquiry Service, PO Box 200, The Open University, Walton Hall, Milton Keynes, MK7 6YZ. If you have not already enrolled on the Course and would like to buy this or other Open University material, please write to Open University Educational Enterprises Ltd, 12 Cofferidge Close, Stony Stratford, Milton Keynes, MK11 1BY, United Kingdom.

1.4

CONTENTS

INTRODUCTION

This unit differs from the others in the course in that it seeks to show how complex analysis may be used in the mathematical modelling of a physical process, namely, the flow of a *fluid* such as water or air.

If you have had experience of mathematical modelling, then the approach adopted here will be familiar to you, in that an initial simplification of a real-world situation is required before we are able to express what is going on mathematically and make progress by means of posing and solving problems. Later we interpret the solutions in physical terms, and conclude by analysing how good the model is and where it could be improved.

If you have not done mathematical modelling before, you need not feel apprehensive about it. This unit may be treated primarily as a mathematics text, although it will help your appreciation of the subject matter if you are able to think in terms of physical quantities such as *velocity* and *pressure*.

When mathematical modelling is carried out 'for real', it is not always clear at the outset which body of mathematical knowledge to apply to the real-world problem being faced. The topic of fluid flows, however, has been chosen precisely because, when various modelling assumptions are made, it can be viewed as an application of complex analysis.

Although the assumptions required to achieve our mathematical end are quite restrictive, the resulting model is still significant, both historically and in terms of the physical insights which it provides. More 'realistic' models of fluid flows have been developed, but their additional realism is paid for by an increase in mathematical complexity. The model considered here has the virtue of being non-trivial but of sufficient simplicity for its predictions to be illuminating. For example, the model predicts correctly the swerve on a spinning ball projected through the air, and the presence of the upward force which keeps an aeroplane in flight.

This same simple model of fluid flows can be developed mathematically without the benefit of complex analysis, but the natural relationships within it cannot then be exhibited in quite such a transparent manner. Complex analysis is a natural language with which to describe this particular model.

In Section 1 we set up the mathematical model for fluid flows, using a complex-valued function to describe the steady fluid *velocity* within a cross-sectional plane. It turns out that, under suitable modelling assumptions, the *conjugate* of the velocity function is *analytic*; this opens up a range of possibilities for the application of previously established mathematical results.

In particular, the conjugate velocity function has a *primitive* (on a suitable region) known as a *complex potential* function, which we introduce in Section 2. The *streamlines*, or paths of points moving with the fluid, can be described simply in terms of the complex potential. In the audio tape in Subsection 2.2 we look at several examples of simple fluid flows, and derive their complex potentials and the corresponding streamline patterns.

In Section 3 we turn to the investigation of flow patterns in a stream passing around a solid object or *obstacle*, covering in detail the case of flow past a circular cylinder. We then show how the theory of *conformal mappings* may be used to link the results for a circular cylinder to those for obstacles of other shapes.

In certain circumstances, the pattern of flow velocity past an obstacle gives rise to a *force* on the obstacle, and Section 4 demonstrates how this force may be calculated. The study of flow past *aerofoils*, which was introduced as an important special case in Section 3, is continued in Section 4. Finally, we take stock of how well the predictions of the model compare with reality.

Study guide

Section 3 forms the most important as well as the heaviest part of this unit, and you will probably need to spend almost half of your study time on it. You should find that Section 2 (which contains the audio tape) is relatively light, although essential in terms of building up your ability to visualize how fluids in motion behave according to the model. Subsections 4.3 and 4.4 are intended for reading only.

1 SETTING UP THE MODEL

After working through this section, you should be able to:

(a) appreciate the modelling assumptions which are made in order to represent fluid flow velocity by a continuous complex function;

(b) apply the formula for the *components* of velocity at any point, in the direction specified by $e^{i\theta}$;

(c) explain what is meant by *stagnation point, streamline, unit-speed parametrization, circulation, flux, locally circulation-free, locally flux-free, model flow, source, sink* and *vortex*;

(d) understand why the conjugate of a model flow velocity function is an analytic function, and conversely;

(e) establish whether a velocity function is locally circulation-free, locally flux-free, or both.

1.1 A complex-valued velocity function

The aim of this unit is to develop a mathematical model which can be applied to the *flow* (or motion) of a *fluid*. *Webster's Dictionary* defines a 'fluid' as 'a substance that alters its shape in response to any force however small, that tends to flow or to conform to the outline of its container, and that includes gases and liquids ...'. Both water (a liquid) and air (a gas) are fluids, and your everyday experience of how these substances behave in motion should give you some feeling for what we intend to model.

One way of visualizing a fluid flow is shown in Figure 1.1 below. The diagram represents a cross-section, at a particular instant in time, of the flow of some fluid (water, say).

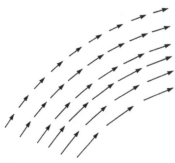

Figure 1.1

Each arrow in this diagram represents the instantaneous *velocity* of the fluid at the point from which the arrow is directed. The magnitude of this velocity (that is, the fluid speed) is represented by the length of the arrow, while the flow direction is given by the direction of the arrow.

Velocity is a *vector* quantity; that is, it has both magnitude and direction.

Photographs of flows rather similar to Figure 1.1 (but without the arrowheads) may be obtained by the insertion of small neutrally buoyant beads into the flow. Exposure of the film for a short interval of time results in the movements of the beads showing up as streaks on the photograph. Since the beads are carried along by the fluid, the streak lengths and directions indicate fluid velocity, as represented above by the arrows.

A 'neutrally buoyant' bead has the same density as that of the fluid, so that it neither rises nor sinks relative to the immediately surrounding fluid.

Suppose that we regard the flow cross-section shown in Figure 1.1 as lying in a region of the complex plane. Then each point in the region can be described by a complex number $z = x + iy$. Since the flow velocity at the point z, like the arrow which represents it, is characterized completely by its magnitude and direction, it can be represented by a complex number $q(z)$, where $|q(z)|$ is the fluid speed at z and $\text{Arg}(q(z))$ is the direction of flow at the point.

Here we mean a region in the sense defined in *Unit A3*, Subsection 4.4. More is said about this below.

The letter q is a traditional symbol for fluid velocity.

Examples of points z and corresponding velocities $q(z)$, for some flow, are shown in Figure 1.2.

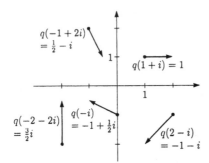

Figure 1.2

At a point z where the fluid is at rest (has zero speed), the flow velocity satisfies $q(z) = 0$. Such a point is called a **stagnation point** of the flow.

Treating z now as a complex variable, we see that in principle the velocities at all points within the fluid cross-section can be described by a complex function q, whose domain is the region occupied by the fluid. Before proceeding further, we note that the use of a complex function q to describe the fluid velocity pattern relies upon several significant *modelling assumptions*.

First, Figure 1.1 depicts a cross-section of a flow which must in reality be three-dimensional, although the two-dimensional diagram is intended to show all the significant features of the flow. You should imagine that a 'point moving with the fluid', which at any time lies in the particular plane shown, continues to reside in that plane at all later times. Moreover, any cross-section of the flow which is parallel to the chosen plane gives a velocity pattern identical to that in the original plane. Such a flow is called *two-dimensional*.

When we speak of a 'point moving with the fluid', we mean the trajectory taken by a small volume of fluid containing the point, in the limit as the volume size tends to zero. It may be easiest to visualize such a 'moving fluid point' as the centre of a (very small) neutrally buoyant bead carried along by the flow.

A second and more basic modelling assumption becomes apparent when we recall that a region of the complex plane is a connected open set. This implies that a region has no 'local gaps'. Our model therefore assumes that the fluid forms a *continuum*, with any point of the region having a specific fluid velocity allocated to it. We shall assume further that the fluid velocity varies continuously in any direction, so that the function q is continuous.

The third main modelling assumption concerns what happens when the fluid moves on from the pattern captured at a particular instant in Figure 1.1. In general, the fluid velocity $q(z)$ at each point z will change with time. This complication is avoided by assuming that the flow is *steady*; this means that, for each fixed point z, the corresponding fluid velocity $q(z)$ is independent of time. Thus Figure 1.1 represents the flow pattern at any time.

According to *Webster's Dictionary*, a 'continuum' is 'an ideal substance or medium containing no vacant spaces and devoid of discrete structure'. In the context of fluids, the continuum hypothesis means that any volume, however small, is assumed to contain some matter. This assumption, and that of continuous velocity variation, describe real fluid situations accurately except at microscopic scales.

Note that the assumption of steady flow is *not* the same as restricting the velocity of a point moving with the fluid to be constant as time passes. What is fixed is the flow velocity observed at any specified point z of the flow region.

We now summarize the basic features of our mathematical model for fluid flows.

Basic Mathematical Model

We assume that

(i) the fluid forms a continuum, and any spatial variation of the flow velocity is continuous;

(ii) the flow is two-dimensional;

(iii) the flow is steady.

With these assumptions, we may represent the flow velocity at all times by a continuous complex function q, whose domain is the region occupied by the fluid.

The requirements that the flow be both two-dimensional and steady may seem too restrictive, since there are many possible flows which are excluded. However, there are significant types of flow which satisfy these conditions, at least approximately; for example, the motion of air past an aeroplane wing in flight can for many purposes be modelled satisfactorily by a two-dimensional steady flow.

Example 1.1

Sketch the arrow pattern for the flow with velocity function

$$q(z) = e^{i\pi/4} \qquad (z \in \mathbb{C}).$$

Solution

For each z, the flow has speed $\left|e^{i\pi/4}\right| = 1$ and direction given by $\mathrm{Arg}\left(e^{i\pi/4}\right) = \pi/4$. The arrow pattern is therefore as shown in Figure 1.3. ■

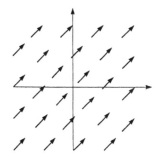

Figure 1.3

Remark The flow in this example is called a **uniform flow**, because the velocity function is a constant function.

Figure 1.3 was easy to draw, because all the arrows were the same length. When the arrow lengths (representing flow speeds) vary widely, it may not be a straightforward matter to sketch this type of picture. For this reason such diagrams are often drawn with arrows of fixed length, representing the direction of the flow at each point but not variations in speed. You are asked to adopt this approach in the next problem.

Problem 1.1

Sketch the arrow pattern, using arrows of fixed length, for each of the following velocity functions.

(a) $q(z) = z \qquad (z \in \mathbb{C})$

(b) $q(z) = i/\bar{z} \qquad (z \in \mathbb{C} - \{0\})$

Determining the velocity function is a main aim for any fluid flow problem posed within the Basic Mathematical Model. As you will see, the velocity function can then be used to obtain a visual representation of the actual motion of the fluid.

To be more precise, the trajectory followed by a point moving with the fluid forms a path $\Gamma : \gamma(t)$ $(t \in I)$, which is called a *streamline*. At any point $\gamma(t)$ on the streamline, the velocity is $q(\gamma(t))$ and this must be equal to $\gamma'(t)$, the rate of change of position, which is a tangent vector to the streamline (see *Unit A4*, page 32). Therefore we make the following definition.

Definition A **streamline** through the point z_0, for a flow with velocity function q, is a smooth path $\Gamma : \gamma(t)$ $(t \in I)$ such that

(a) $\gamma'(t) = q(\gamma(t)),$ for $t \in I$;

(b) $z_0 = \gamma(t_0),$ for some $t_0 \in I$.

If $q(z_0) = 0$ (that is, if z_0 is a stagnation point), then $\{z_0\}$ is a **degenerate streamline**, with constant parametrization

$$\gamma(t) = z_0 \qquad (t \in I).$$

The term 'smooth path' and the interpretation of $\gamma'(t)$ as a tangent vector to the path $\Gamma : \gamma$ at the point $\gamma(t)$ were introduced in *Unit A4*, Subsection 4.1.

Remarks

1 Any such path $\Gamma : \gamma$ has infinitely many equivalent parametrizations which differ from γ only by a time translation (that is, by having the image z_0 at a different value of t_0). This corresponds to the fact that, for a steady flow, a description of the flow pattern is unaffected by the moment at which you choose to set a clock to measure time.

2 Note that streamlines need not be straight lines. In the mathematical context, they are also called *flow lines*.

As an example, consider the flow velocity function $q(z) = e^{i\pi/4}$ $(z \in \mathbb{C})$, from Example 1.1. In this case, Condition (a) is

$$\gamma'(t) = q(\gamma(t)) = e^{i\pi/4},$$

so a streamline through the point z_0 is given by the parametrization

$$\gamma(t) = z_0 + t e^{i\pi/4} \qquad (t \in \mathbb{R}).$$

Here we have $t_0 = 0$.

To return to the general situation, note that we may use Condition (a) to sketch streamlines. At each point z, the velocity $q(z)$ is a tangent vector to a streamline which passes through z (unless z is a stagnation point). For example, we constructed the streamline picture in Figure 1.4 by 'joining up the arrows' of the flow pattern in Figure 1.1. We indicate the flow direction along each streamline by a single arrowhead.

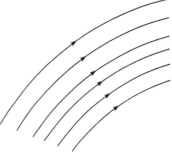

Figure 1.4

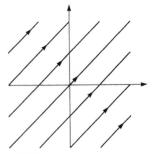

Figure 1.5

Similarly, the streamlines for the flow of Example 1.1 are shown in Figure 1.5.

Problem 1.2

Sketch a few streamlines for each of the flows whose velocities are given in Problem 1.1.

1.2 Developing the model

We have assumed that we can restrict attention to the steady, two-dimensional flow of a fluid forming a continuum, for which the fluid velocity throughout its flow domain is represented by a continuous complex function q. We now make two further modelling assumptions in order to represent the physical situation with a greater degree of accuracy, and to make more specific the mathematical problem of finding the flow velocity function q for given circumstances.

In order to describe these restrictions, we need to introduce the ideas of *circulation* and *flux*. As a necessary preliminary to this, we derive a useful expression for the *component* of velocity in a given direction and introduce a particularly convenient type of parametrization.

The *component* of a vector in a given direction is its (scalar) perpendicular projection onto that direction.

Suppose that the given direction is at an angle θ anticlockwise from the positive real axis, so that it may be specified by the complex number $e^{i\theta}$. Here $e^{i\theta}$ acts as a unit vector in the chosen direction, since $\left|e^{i\theta}\right| = 1$.

Let $q(z)$ be the complex number representing the velocity at a point z. Figure 1.6 shows two cases of how $q_\theta(z)$, the component of $q(z)$ in the direction specified by $e^{i\theta}$, is obtained by projecting $q(z)$ perpendicularly onto that direction.

Note that the component $q_\theta(z)$ may be positive, negative or zero, depending on whether the smallest angle between $q(z)$ and $e^{i\theta}$ has magnitude less than, greater than or equal to $\pi/2$, respectively.

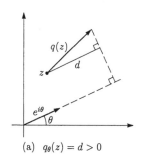

(a) $\quad q_\theta(z) = d > 0$ (b) $\quad q_\theta(z) = -d < 0$

Figure 1.6

We now seek an expression for the component $q_\theta(z)$ in terms of $q(z)$ and θ. If we rotate both the complex number $q(z)$ and the θ direction line clockwise about z through the angle θ, then $q(z)$ goes to $q(z)e^{-i\theta}$ and the θ direction line becomes parallel to the real axis. This is shown in Figure 1.7 for the situation in Figure 1.6(a). Now the component of $q(z)e^{-i\theta}$ in the positive x-direction is

$$\mathrm{Re}\left(q(z)e^{-i\theta}\right),$$

and this is the same number as the component $q_\theta(z)$. Hence

$$q_\theta(z) = \mathrm{Re}\left(q(z)e^{-i\theta}\right).$$

This last equation gives an expression for the component $q_\theta(z)$ of $q(z)$ in the direction specified by $e^{i\theta}$. It turns out that a variation of this formula is more useful. This variation depends on the fact that the real parts of a complex number and of its conjugate are the same, so that we have

$$q_\theta(z) = \mathrm{Re}\left(\overline{q(z)e^{-i\theta}}\right) = \mathrm{Re}\left(\overline{q(z)}\,e^{i\theta}\right). \tag{1.1}$$

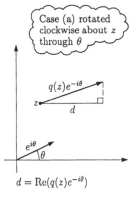

Case (a) rotated clockwise about z through θ

$$d = \mathrm{Re}(q(z)e^{-i\theta})$$

Figure 1.7

Example 1.2

Find the component of $q(z) = 2i$ (at any point z) in the direction specified by $e^{i\pi/6}$.

Solution

From Equation (1.1), with $q(z) = 2i$ and $\theta = \pi/6$, we have

$$q_{\pi/6}(z) = \mathrm{Re}\left(\overline{2i}\,e^{i\pi/6}\right)$$

$$= \mathrm{Re}\left(-2i\left(\cos\frac{\pi}{6} + i\sin\frac{\pi}{6}\right)\right)$$

$$= 2\sin\frac{\pi}{6} = 1. \quad\blacksquare$$

Problem 1.3

Find the component of $q(z) = 5e^{-i\pi/6}$ (at any point z) in the direction specified by $e^{2i\pi/3}$.

Problem 1.4

Use Equation (1.1) to show that the component of velocity $q(z)$ in the direction at angle $\pi/2$ clockwise to that of $e^{i\theta}$ can be expressed as

$$q_{(\theta - \pi/2)}(z) = \mathrm{Im}\left(\overline{q(z)}e^{i\theta}\right).$$

Equation (1.1) and the result of Problem 1.4 can be rewritten in terms of the **conjugate velocity function** $\bar{q}$, which has the same domain as q and rule

$$\bar{q}(z) = \overline{q(z)}.$$

We have

$$q_\theta(z) = \mathrm{Re}\left(\bar{q}(z)e^{i\theta}\right) \quad \text{and} \quad q_{(\theta - \pi/2)}(z) = \mathrm{Im}\left(\bar{q}(z)e^{i\theta}\right), \qquad (1.2)$$

which will be of use shortly.

For example, if $q(z) = iz$, then
$$\bar{q}(z) = \overline{iz} = -i\bar{z}.$$

Now suppose that $\Gamma : \gamma(t)$ $(t \in I)$ is a smooth path of finite length lying in the domain of a flow velocity function q. We wish to define two quantities, circulation and flux, associated with Γ and q, and it will be convenient to assume that γ is a **unit-speed parametrization**; that is,

$$|\gamma'(t)| = 1, \qquad \text{for } t \in I.$$

The following result shows that we can always do this.

Note that Γ is not necessarily part of a streamline.

For example,
$$\gamma(t) = 2\left(\cos \tfrac{1}{2}t + i \sin \tfrac{1}{2}t\right)$$
$$(t \in [0, 4\pi])$$
is a unit-speed parametrization of the circle $|z| = 2$.

Theorem 1.1 If $\Gamma : \gamma_1(t)$ $(t \in [a, b])$ is a smooth path of length L, then there is an equivalent parametrization $\gamma(s)$ $(s \in [0, L])$ such that

$$|\gamma'(s)| = 1, \qquad \text{for } 0 \le s \le L. \qquad (1.3)$$

Proof Since γ_1 is smooth, the real function $t \longmapsto |\gamma_1'(t)|$ is continuous on $[a, b]$, and so it has a primitive h, say. Assuming, as we may, that $h(a) = 0$, we obtain

$$h(b) = h(b) - h(a) = \int_a^b |\gamma_1'(u)|\,du = L,$$

by the Fundamental Theorem of Calculus. Because $h'(t) = |\gamma_1'(t)| > 0$, we deduce that the function $\gamma(s) = \gamma_1\left(h^{-1}(s)\right)$ $(s \in [0, L])$ is an equivalent parametrization with

$$|\gamma'(s)| = \left|\gamma_1'\left(h^{-1}(s)\right)\left(h^{-1}\right)'(s)\right| \qquad \text{(Chain Rule)}$$
$$= |\gamma_1'(t)|/h'(t) \qquad \text{(Inverse Function Rule} : t = h^{-1}(s))$$
$$= 1, \qquad \text{for } 0 \le s \le L,$$

as required. ∎

Unit B1, Frame 5

$$\left(h^{-1}\right)'(s) = \frac{1}{h'(h^{-1}(s))}$$
$$= \frac{1}{h'(t)}.$$

Remark If Equation (1.3) holds, then the parameter s measures length along Γ since, if $0 \le s_1 < s_2 \le L$, then the length of Γ from $\gamma(s_1)$ to $\gamma(s_2)$ is

$$\int_{s_1}^{s_2} |\gamma'(s)|\,ds = \int_{s_1}^{s_2} 1\,ds = s_2 - s_1.$$

Note that it is traditional to use the letter s as parameter with unit-speed parametrizations.

The use of unit-speed parametrizations makes it possible to define the tangential and normal components of a flow velocity function q at a point on a smooth path Γ.

Definitions If $\Gamma : \gamma(s)$ ($s \in [0, L]$) is a smooth path with unit-speed parametrization, which lies in the region $\mathcal{R}$ of a flow velocity function q, then, for each $s \in [0, L]$, the flow velocity $q(\gamma(s))$ has

(a) **tangential component** $q_T(s)$ in the direction specified by $\gamma'(s)$;

(b) **normal component** $q_N(s)$ in the direction specified by $-i\gamma'(s)$.

These components are shown in Figure 1.8 in a case when both are positive.

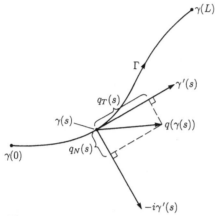

Figure 1.8

Note that $\gamma'(s)$ is a *unit* tangent vector at the point $\gamma(s)$ on Γ, for each $s \in [0, L]$, and $-i\gamma'(s)$ is a unit normal vector.

We now define *circulation* and *flux* in terms of these velocity components.

Definitions Let Γ be a smooth path of length L in the domain of a flow velocity function q, and let $\gamma : [0, L] \longrightarrow \Gamma$ be the equivalent unit-speed parametrization of Γ.

(a) The **circulation** of q along Γ is

$$C_\Gamma = \int_0^L q_T(s)\, ds. \qquad (1.4)$$

(b) The **flux** of q across Γ is

$$\mathcal{F}_\Gamma = \int_0^L q_N(s)\, ds. \qquad (1.5)$$

Note that these are real integrals, so both the circulation C_Γ and the flux $\mathcal{F}_\Gamma$ are real quantities.

In words, the circulation of q along Γ is

  $L \times$ the average value of q_T on Γ,

and the flux of q across Γ is

  $L \times$ the average value of q_N on Γ.

In physical terms, flux is a measure of the overall rate at which fluid is crossing Γ.

(You will be asked to calculate a circulation and a flux in Problem 1.7.)

Now for each $s \in [0, L]$, $\gamma'(s)$ has modulus 1, and so we have $\gamma'(s) = e^{i\theta}$ for some θ. Thus

$$q_T(s) = q_\theta(\gamma(s)) \qquad \text{and} \qquad q_N(s) = q_{(\theta - \pi/2)}(\gamma(s)),$$

so that, by Equations (1.2),

$$q_T(s) = \mathrm{Re}(\overline{q}(\gamma(s))\gamma'(s)) \qquad \text{and} \qquad q_N(s) = \mathrm{Im}(\overline{q}(\gamma(s))\gamma'(s)). \qquad (1.6)$$

It follows from the definitions of circulation and flux, in Equations (1.4) and (1.5), that

$$\mathcal{C}_\Gamma + i\mathcal{F}_\Gamma = \int_0^L (q_T(s) + iq_N(s))\,ds$$
$$= \int_0^L \overline{q}(\gamma(s))\gamma'(s)\,ds;$$

that is,

$$\mathcal{C}_\Gamma + i\mathcal{F}_\Gamma = \int_\Gamma \overline{q}(z)\,dz. \tag{1.7}$$

In deriving this formula, we assumed for simplicity that the path Γ has a unit-speed parametrization. However the formula is valid also with any equivalent parametrization for the path. Furthermore, this result for smooth paths can be extended easily to a corresponding result for contours. Indeed, Equation (1.7) holds for any contour Γ, provided that the circulation $\mathcal{C}_\Gamma$ is defined as the sum of the circulations along the smooth paths which form Γ, and the flux $\mathcal{F}_\Gamma$ is defined as the sum of the fluxes across these smooth paths.

This is a consequence of *Unit B1*, Theorem 2.1.

We are now almost ready to make the final modelling assumptions. These are based on the following definitions.

Definitions   A velocity function q with domain a region $\mathcal{R}$ is

(a) **locally circulation-free** if $\mathcal{C}_\Gamma = 0$ for each simple-closed contour Γ in $\mathcal{R}$ whose inside also lies in $\mathcal{R}$;

(b) **locally flux-free** if $\mathcal{F}_\Gamma = 0$ for each simple-closed contour Γ in $\mathcal{R}$ whose inside also lies in $\mathcal{R}$.

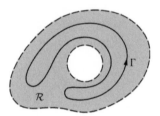

Figure 1.9

Remarks

1 Figure 1.9 shows such a contour Γ in a region $\mathcal{R}$ which is not simply-connected. Note that if $\mathcal{R}$ is simply-connected, then the inside of any simple-closed contour in $\mathcal{R}$ automatically lies in $\mathcal{R}$.

2 The word 'locally' occurs here because, for each point $z \in \mathcal{R}$, the condition that the inside of the contour Γ should lie within $\mathcal{R}$ is satisfied automatically if Γ lies in any open disc in $\mathcal{R}$ with centre at z.

We shall assume for our model that any flow to be considered has a velocity function which satisfies both of the conditions just defined.

Definition   A **model flow** of a fluid is described by a continuous complex velocity function (whose domain is a region) which is locally circulation-free and locally flux-free.

The locally flux-free condition is equivalent (for a constant-density fluid) to the *Principle of Conservation of Mass*, which states that mass (matter) is neither created nor destroyed. In the context of fluid flows this means the following: for any simple-closed contour Γ whose inside is in the flow region $\mathcal{R}$, and at any time, any flow of fluid mass (per unit depth) inwards across Γ must be exactly balanced by a mass flow outwards, so that the mass of fluid associated with the inside of Γ remains constant.

In vector calculus notation, the locally flux-free condition is expressed as
$$\operatorname{div}\mathbf{q} = 0.$$

The need for the locally circulation-free condition is less obvious, and indeed there are actual flows, satisfying approximately all of the other specified conditions, which are *not* locally circulation-free. Roughly speaking, this condition permits us to restrict attention from all the possible flows for a given situation to the unique flow among them which has 'minimum energy' associated with it. In fact, in terms of a small neutrally buoyant bead, whose surface velocity matches that of the adjacent fluid, the locally circulation-free

In vector calculus notation, the locally circulation-free condition is expressed as
$$\operatorname{curl}\mathbf{q} = \mathbf{0}.$$

By a 'given situation' here, we mean the specified configuration of physical boundaries for the flow, limiting flow speed at large distances, and so on.

condition means that *the bead will not rotate*. In other words, the flow has no 'swirl' or 'local angular velocity'. For this reason, a flow with this property is also called *irrotational*.

It follows immediately from Equation (1.7) that

a fluid flow is a model flow on a region $\mathcal{R}$ if and only if its velocity function q satisfies the condition

$$\int_\Gamma \overline{q}(z)\,dz = 0,$$

for each simple-closed contour Γ in $\mathcal{R}$ whose inside also lies in $\mathcal{R}$.

This important fact will be applied in the next subsection.

In vector calculus notation, the condition for the imaginary part of this equation is equivalent to $\operatorname{div}\mathbf{q} = 0$, via Gauss' Divergence Theorem. The condition for the real part is equivalent to $\operatorname{curl}\mathbf{q} = \mathbf{0}$, via Stokes' Theorem (or Green's Theorem in the Plane).

1.3 The conjugate velocity function

Our model flow is described by a continuous velocity function q, whose domain is a region $\mathcal{R}$. As pointed out in the previous subsection, the conjugate velocity function $\overline{q}$ may be defined by

$$\overline{q}(z) = \overline{q(z)} \qquad (z \in \mathcal{R}).$$

The function $\overline{q}$ is continuous, since q is continuous.

Note that
$$\overline{\overline{q}(z)} = q(z).$$

Now, by our assumptions, q is locally both circulation-free and flux-free. Hence, as you saw above, we have

$$\int_\Gamma \overline{q}(z)\,dz = 0, \tag{1.8}$$

for each simple-closed contour Γ in $\mathcal{R}$ whose inside lies in $\mathcal{R}$. In particular, Equation (1.8) holds for all rectangular contours whose insides lie in $\mathcal{R}$, and so it follows from Morera's Theorem that the conjugate velocity function $\overline{q}$ is analytic on $\mathcal{R}$.

Unit B2, Theorem 5.4

The converse of this result also holds. If g is any function analytic on a region $\mathcal{R}$ then, by Cauchy's Theorem,

Unit B2, Theorem 1.2

$$\int_\Gamma g(z)\,dz = 0,$$

for each simple-closed contour Γ whose inside lies in $\mathcal{R}$. By Equation (1.7), the function q defined by $\overline{q}(z) = g(z)$ must then be locally both circulation-free and flux-free. We have thus established the following result.

Theorem 1.2 A steady two-dimensional fluid flow with continuous velocity function q on a region $\mathcal{R}$ is a model flow if and only if its conjugate velocity function $\overline{q}$ is analytic on $\mathcal{R}$.

This theorem provides a method for finding a profusion of model fluid flows, since the conjugate of each analytic function provides a corresponding model flow velocity function.

Example 1.3

Find the model flow velocity function corresponding to the analytic function

$$g(z) = e^{-i\pi/4} \qquad (z \in \mathbb{C}).$$

Solution

The conjugate velocity function is $\overline{q}(z) = e^{-i\pi/4}$, so that the model flow velocity function is

$$q(z) = e^{i\pi/4} \qquad (z \in \mathbb{C}). \quad \blacksquare$$

The streamlines for this flow are shown in Figure 1.5.

Problem 1.5

For each of the following analytic functions g, find the corresponding model flow velocity function. Draw a fixed length arrow pattern to illustrate each answer.

(a) $g(z) = z$ $(z \in \mathbb{C})$

(b) $g(z) = 1/z$ $(z \in \mathbb{C} - \{0\})$

(c) $g(z) = i/z$ $(z \in \mathbb{C} - \{0\})$

Problem 1.6

Which of the velocity functions specified in Problem 1.1 represents a model fluid flow?

Problem 1.7

Let Γ be the unit circle $\{z : |z| = 1\}$.

(a) Use Equation (1.7) to find the flux across Γ of the velocity function which you found in Problem 1.5(b).

(b) Use Equation (1.7) to find the circulation along Γ of the velocity function which you found in Problem 1.5(c).

(c) Explain why your answers to parts (a) and (b) do not contradict Theorem 1.2.

Problem 1.7 demonstrates that the flux or circulation of a flow may be non-zero for certain closed contours even when the flow is *locally* both circulation-free and flux-free. The example of Problem 1.5(b) features a *source* of strength $\mathcal{F}_\Gamma = 2\pi$ at the origin, corresponding to outward flow, whereas that of Problem 1.5(c) features a *vortex* of strength $\mathcal{C}_\Gamma = -2\pi$ at the origin, corresponding to clockwise flow. More generally, we have the following definitions, which are illustrated by Figure 1.10.

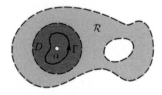

Figure 1.10

Definitions Let q be a model flow velocity function with domain a region $\mathcal{R}$, and let D be a punctured open disc in $\mathcal{R}$ with centre α. Then

(a) α is a **source** of strength $\mathcal{F}$ if $\mathcal{F}_\Gamma = \mathcal{F} \neq 0$ for each simple-closed contour Γ in D which surrounds α;

(b) α is a **vortex** of strength $\mathcal{C}$ if $\mathcal{C}_\Gamma = \mathcal{C} \neq 0$ for each simple-closed contour Γ in D which surrounds α.

Remarks

1 If the point α is a source or a vortex, then it is not in the region $\mathcal{R}$. In fact, $\bar{q}$ then has an isolated singularity at α (*Unit B4*, Subsection 1.1).

2 The fact that $\mathcal{F}_\Gamma$ and $\mathcal{C}_\Gamma$ are independent of the choice of the simple-closed contour Γ is a consequence of the Shrinking Contour Theorem (*Unit B2*, Theorem 1.4).

3 In these definitions, $\mathcal{F}$ and $\mathcal{C}$ may be positive or negative. A source of negative strength is called a **sink**, since fluid is then flowing in to the point α rather than out from it. Negative vortex strength indicates clockwise rather than anticlockwise flow.

To conclude this section, we ask you to use the Cauchy–Riemann equations to obtain an alternative formulation of the condition that a model flow velocity function should be locally both circulation-free and flux-free.

Unit A4, Subsection 2.1

Problem 1.8

(a) Let q be a continuous complex velocity function with domain a region $\mathcal{R}$, and suppose that $q_1 = \operatorname{Re} q$ and $q_2 = \operatorname{Im} q$ have partial derivatives with respect to x and y which are continuous on $\mathcal{R}$.

Prove that q is a model flow velocity function on $\mathcal{R}$ if and only if

$$\frac{\partial q_1}{\partial x} + \frac{\partial q_2}{\partial y} = 0 \quad \text{and} \quad \frac{\partial q_2}{\partial x} - \frac{\partial q_1}{\partial y} = 0 \quad \text{on } \mathcal{R}.$$

Here we are treating q_1 and q_2 as functions of (x, y) rather than of $z = x + iy$.

(b) Use your result from part (a) to verify that the function

$$q(z) = i/\bar{z} \quad (z \in \mathbb{C} - \{0\})$$

of Problem 1.1(b) represents a model flow.

Remark The two equations in Problem 1.8(a) can be used to show that if q is a model flow velocity function, then both the following equations hold:

$$\frac{\partial^2 q_1}{\partial x^2} + \frac{\partial^2 q_1}{\partial y^2} = 0 \quad \text{and} \quad \frac{\partial^2 q_2}{\partial x^2} + \frac{\partial^2 q_2}{\partial y^2} = 0 \quad \text{on } \mathcal{R}.$$

Thus both q_1 and q_2 satisfy the second-order partial differential equation

$$\frac{\partial^2 u}{\partial x^2} + \frac{\partial^2 u}{\partial y^2} = 0,$$

Here $\partial^2 q_1/\partial x^2$, for example, is the second partial derivative of q_1 with respect to x, that is, the second derivative of q_1 with respect to x while keeping y constant.

which is called **Laplace's Equation**. Functions which are solutions of Laplace's Equation are called **harmonic**. Thus the real and imaginary parts of any model flow velocity function are harmonic, as are the real and imaginary parts of any analytic function.

Pierre Simon Laplace (1749–1827) was a leading French mathematician and astronomer.

You showed in Problem 1.8(a) that a function q is a model flow velocity function (that is, locally both circulation-free and flux-free) if and only if the two partial differential equations given in the problem both hold. In fact, this result can be split into two constituent parts, though we shall not prove this.

Theorem 1.3 Let q be a continuous complex velocity function on a region $\mathcal{R}$, and suppose that $q_1 = \operatorname{Re} q$ and $q_2 = \operatorname{Im} q$ have partial derivatives with respect to x and y which are continuous on $\mathcal{R}$. Then q is

(a) locally circulation-free on $\mathcal{R}$ if and only if

$$\frac{\partial q_2}{\partial x} - \frac{\partial q_1}{\partial y} = 0 \quad \text{on } \mathcal{R};$$

(b) locally flux-free on $\mathcal{R}$ if and only if

$$\frac{\partial q_1}{\partial x} + \frac{\partial q_2}{\partial y} = 0 \quad \text{on } \mathcal{R}.$$

In vector calculus notation, these conditions may be written respectively as

(a) $\operatorname{curl} \mathbf{q} = \mathbf{0}$;

(b) $\operatorname{div} \mathbf{q} = 0$.

These conditions on q_1 and q_2 are often easier to apply than the original definitions of locally flux-free and locally circulation-free, especially when only one of these properties holds.

Problem 1.9

Use Theorem 1.3 to show that

(a) the flow velocity function $q(z) = z$ of Problem 1.1(a) is locally circulation-free, but is not locally flux-free;

(b) the flow velocity function $q(z) = iz$ is locally flux-free, but is not locally circulation-free.

In the next section you will see further consequences of the close link between model fluid flows and analytic functions.

2 COMPLEX POTENTIAL FUNCTIONS

After working through this section, you should be able to:

(a) understand and apply the definition of the *complex potential function*;

(b) find families of streamlines, using the complex potential function or *stream function*;

(c) recognize complex potentials for a source, sink or vortex flow;

(d) appreciate the main features of a flow involving a *doublet*, and the effect of placing a doublet in a uniform flow.

2.1 An equation for streamlines

For the rest of this unit we deal only with model fluid flows, for which Theorem 1.2 provides a fruitful connection to the theory of analytic functions. You have already seen how this link can be applied either to generate model flow velocity functions or to test, using the Cauchy–Riemann equations, whether a velocity function does indeed describe a model fluid flow.

We look next at the application to fluid flows of another important result for analytic functions, namely, the Primitive (or Antiderivative) Theorem, which states that if a function is analytic on a simply-connected region $\mathcal{R}$, then it has a primitive on $\mathcal{R}$.

Unit B2, Theorem 5.3

Suppose that q is a model flow velocity function with domain $\mathcal{R}$. Then, by Theorem 1.2, the conjugate velocity function $\bar{q}$ is an analytic function, with the same domain $\mathcal{R}$. Now $\mathcal{R}$ may not be simply-connected, but if $\mathcal{S}$ is a simply-connected subregion of $\mathcal{R}$ then, according to the Primitive Theorem, $\bar{q}$ has a primitive function Ω, say, on $\mathcal{S}$. In other words, there exists a function Ω, analytic on its domain $\mathcal{S}$, such that

$$\Omega'(z) = \bar{q}(z), \qquad \text{for } z \in \mathcal{S}.$$

In the context of model fluid flows, a function Ω which is a primitive of $\bar{q}$ is called a **complex potential function** for the flow. By taking the complex conjugate of the equation above, we see that the flow velocity function q is given in terms of the complex potential function by

$$q(z) = \overline{\Omega'(z)}, \qquad \text{for } z \in \mathcal{S}.$$

Often this is abbreviated to 'complex potential'. The use of the Greek letter Ω (capital omega) for the complex potential function is traditional in the study of fluid dynamics.

The significance of the complex potential function requires some explanation. First, note that, from Equation (1.7), we have

$$\mathcal{C}_\Gamma + i\mathcal{F}_\Gamma = \int_\Gamma \bar{q}(z)\,dz,$$

where $\mathcal{C}_\Gamma$ and $\mathcal{F}_\Gamma$ are, respectively, the circulation along and flux across any contour Γ in $\mathcal{R}$. Now, provided that Γ lies within the simply-connected subregion $\mathcal{S}$ on which the complex potential Ω is defined, we may apply the Fundamental Theorem of Calculus to deduce that

Note that Γ need not be a closed contour here.

Unit B1, Theorem 3.1

$$\mathcal{C}_\Gamma + i\mathcal{F}_\Gamma = \int_\Gamma \Omega'(z)\,dz = \Omega(\beta) - \Omega(\alpha), \tag{2.1}$$

where α and β are the initial and final points of Γ. The real and imaginary parts of this equation are, respectively,

$$\mathcal{C}_\Gamma = \operatorname{Re}(\Omega(\beta)) - \operatorname{Re}(\Omega(\alpha)) \qquad \text{and} \qquad \mathcal{F}_\Gamma = \operatorname{Im}(\Omega(\beta)) - \operatorname{Im}(\Omega(\alpha)). \tag{2.2}$$

These formulas show that, for a model flow velocity function, the circulation along (or flux across) any contour within $\mathcal{S}$ from α to β is the same. (This is an example of the Contour Independence Theorem (*Unit B2*, Theorem 1.3).) For example, for the contours shown in Figure 2.1, the integral of $\Omega'(z)$ along the contour Γ_1 and that along Γ_2 are both equal to $\Omega(\beta) - \Omega(\alpha)$.

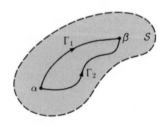

Figure 2.1

Now flux was defined (Equation (1.5)) as the integral along a smooth path $\Gamma : \gamma$ of the normal component $q_N(s)$ of the flow velocity $q(\gamma(s))$. Thus if the flow velocity at each point $\gamma(s)$ of Γ is a tangent vector to the path (so that $q_N(s) = 0$), as shown in Figure 2.2, then there is *zero* flux across Γ. Paths of this type are the trajectories of points moving with the fluid. They were given the name 'streamlines' in Subsection 1.1, where we indicated their usefulness as a means of viewing a fluid flow.

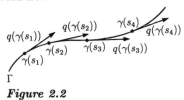

Figure 2.2

A streamline Γ therefore has the property that there is no flux across it. Thus if α and β both lie on a streamline Γ, then, by applying Equation (2.2) to the part of Γ which joins α to β, we have

$$\operatorname{Im}(\Omega(\beta)) = \operatorname{Im}(\Omega(\alpha)).$$

Thus we have proved the following result.

Theorem 2.1 If Ω is a complex potential function on a simply-connected subregion $\mathcal{S}$ of the flow region $\mathcal{R}$, then

$\operatorname{Im}(\Omega(z))$ is constant along each streamline within $\mathcal{S}$.

Remarks

1 This theorem states that, for each streamline Γ in $\mathcal{S}$, there is a constant k such that $\operatorname{Im}(\Omega(z)) = k$ for all $z \in \Gamma$. However, the set $\{z \in \mathcal{S} : \operatorname{Im}(\Omega(z)) = k\}$ may comprise more than one streamline. You will see examples of this type in Subsection 2.2.

2 The result refers to the portion of a streamline Γ within a simply-connected subregion $\mathcal{S}$ of the flow region $\mathcal{R}$. If Γ extends beyond $\mathcal{S}$, then it is possible to cover the extension by an appropriate sequence of simply-connected subregions $\mathcal{S}_n$ with associated complex potentials Ω_n ($n = 1, 2, \ldots$), where $\mathcal{S}_1 = \mathcal{S}$ and $\Omega_1 = \Omega$ (see Figure 2.3). Each complex potential of the sequence after the first is related to the previous one by direct analytic continuation, and the constant value of $\operatorname{Im} \Omega_n$ on Γ will then be the same for each n.

Unit C3, Subsection 1.1

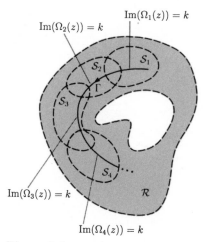

Figure 2.3

3 Theorem 2.1 can also be used to show that each point of the flow region has just one streamline through it. Despite this, it may sometimes *appear* that there are two streamlines passing through a point. This impression can occur only at a stagnation point, which is itself a degenerate streamline.

Theorem 2.1 indicates one reason why complex potential functions are of interest. If

$$\Omega(z) = \Phi(x,y) + i\Psi(x,y), \quad \text{where } z = x + iy,$$

is an analytic function on a simply-connected region $\mathcal{S}$, where Φ, Ψ are real-valued functions, then the family of curves described by the equation

$$\Psi(x,y) = \text{constant}$$

forms the streamlines of a model fluid flow. The function $\Psi = \text{Im}\,\Omega$ is therefore called the **stream function** for the flow.

The use of the Greek letters Φ and Ψ (capital phi and psi) for the real and imaginary parts of Ω is standard practice in fluid dynamics.

In the next subsection we look at several model flows, given by flow velocity functions. In each case we find a complex potential function and then the corresponding stream function.

Problem 2.1

Show that the flow velocity function q may be expressed directly in terms of the stream function Ψ as

$$q(z) = \frac{\partial \Psi}{\partial y} - i\frac{\partial \Psi}{\partial x}.$$

This gives the flow velocity $q(z)$ at z in terms of the stream function Ψ.

Remark For a non-model flow whose velocity function is locally flux-free (but not locally circulation-free), there still exists a stream function Ψ, defined in terms of the velocity function q as in the result of Problem 2.1, for which the streamlines are given by $\Psi(x,y) = \text{constant}$.

However, in this case there is no analytic conjugate velocity function and hence no complex potential; that is, there is no analytic function Ω for which $\Psi = \text{Im}\,\Omega$. Such flows are not considered further in this unit.

2.2 Examples of fluid flows (audio-tape)

This audio tape presents several examples of model fluid flows, some of which you have seen earlier. In each case the starting point is a model flow velocity function, from which we derive a complex potential and the corresponding stream function. This enables the streamline diagram to be drawn. Despite the simplicity of these cases, you will see later that they can be used as the building blocks for more complicated model flows.

NOW START THE TAPE.

3. A source

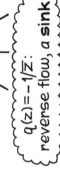

rays

(a) Velocity function:
$$q(z) = \frac{1}{\overline{z}} = \frac{z}{|z|^2} \qquad (z \in \mathbb{C} - \{0\}).$$

(b) Complex potential:
$$\Omega(z) = \text{Log } z$$
$$= \log_e |z| + i \,\text{Arg } z \qquad (z \in \mathbb{C}_\pi).$$

(c) Streamlines:
$$\text{Im}(\Omega(z)) = \boxed{} = \text{constant}.$$

(d) Source strength:
$$\text{Im}\left(\int_\Gamma \overline{q}(z)\,dz\right) = 2\pi.$$

Flux

$q(z) = -1/\overline{z}$: reverse flow, a sink

---

4. A vortex

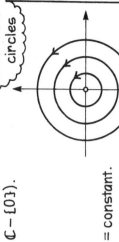

concentric circles

(a) Velocity function:
$$q(z) = \frac{i}{\overline{z}} = \frac{iz}{|z|^2} \qquad (z \in \mathbb{C} - \{0\}).$$

(b) Complex potential:
$$\Omega(z) = -i\,\text{Log } z.$$

(c) Streamlines:
$$\text{Im}(\Omega(z)) = \boxed{} = \text{constant}.$$

(d) Vortex strength:
$$\text{Re}\left(\int_\Gamma \overline{q}(z)\,dz\right) = 2\pi.$$

Circulation

$q(z) = -i/\overline{z}$: clockwise vortex flow

---

1. Uniform flow

parallel lines

$\propto = a + ib \neq 0$

(a) Velocity function:
$$q(z) = \propto.$$

(b) Complex potential:
$$\Omega(z) = \overline{\propto} z.$$

$\Omega'(z) = \overline{q}(z) = \overline{\propto}$

stream function

(c) Streamlines:
$$\text{Im}(\Omega(z)) = \boxed{} = \text{constant}.$$

$$y = \frac{b}{a}x + k \qquad (\text{for } a \neq 0)$$
$$\text{or } x = k.$$

Arg $\propto$

---

2. Flow with a stagnation point

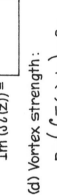

hyperbolas

(a) Velocity function:
$$q(z) = \overline{z}. \qquad q(0) = 0.$$

(b) Complex potential:
$$\Omega(z) = \tfrac{1}{2} z^2.$$

(c) Streamlines:
$$\text{Im}(\Omega(z)) = \boxed{} = \text{constant}.$$

$$xy = k.$$

$q(z) = \propto \overline{z}$: rotate picture through $\frac{1}{2}\text{Arg }\propto$.

Frame 1, Frame 6

7. A doublet in a uniform stream

(a) Velocity function:

$$q(z) = 1 - \frac{a^2}{z^2} \quad (z \in \mathbb{C} - \{0\}).$$

$a > 0$

stagnation points at $\pm a$

(b) Complex potential:

$$\Omega(z) = z + \frac{a^2}{z}.$$

(c) Streamlines:

$$\text{Im}(\Omega(z)) = \boxed{} = \text{constant}.$$

$y = 0$, $x^2 + y^2 = a^2$; or

$$x = \pm\sqrt{\frac{a^2}{1 - k/y} - y^2}$$

(for $k \neq 0$).

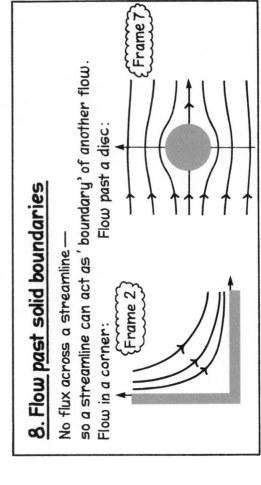

8. Flow past solid boundaries

No flux across a streamline—
so a streamline can act as 'boundary' of another flow.

Flow in a corner: Frame 2

Flow past a disc: Frame 7

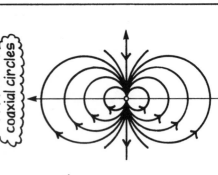
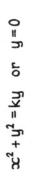

5. Problem 2.2

Determine a complex potential function for the velocity function

$$q(z) = \frac{-1 + 8i}{z}.$$

Hence sketch the streamlines for this flow and determine the corresponding source strength and vortex strength.

6. A doublet

(a) Velocity function:

$$q(z) = -\frac{1}{z^2} = -\frac{\overline{z}^2}{|z|^4} \quad (z \in \mathbb{C} - \{0\}).$$

(b) Complex potential:

$$\Omega(z) = \frac{1}{z} = \frac{\overline{z}}{|z|^2}.$$

(c) Streamlines:

$$\text{Im}(\Omega(z)) = \boxed{} = \text{constant}.$$

$x^2 + y^2 = ky$ or $y = 0$

$x^2 + (y - \frac{1}{2}k)^2 = \frac{1}{4}k^2$ or $y = 0$.

coaxial circles

directional combination of source and sink

Problem 2.3

(a) Let $h > 0$. Show that the model flow velocity function

$$q(z) = \frac{1}{\overline{z}} - \frac{1}{\overline{z} - h}$$

has complex potential function

$$\Omega(z) = \operatorname{Log} z - \operatorname{Log}(z - h) \qquad (z \in \mathbb{C} - \{x \in \mathbb{R} : x \le h\}).$$

This represents the flow resulting from the combination of a source at the origin and a sink at $z = h$, both of strength 2π.

(b) Use elementary geometry to show that the streamlines of this flow are circular arcs terminating at $z = 0$ and $z = h$, with the centres of the circles lying on the line $x = \frac{1}{2}h$.

Problem 2.4

The model flow velocity function

$$q_h(z) = \frac{1}{h}\left(\frac{1}{\overline{z}} - \frac{1}{\overline{z} - h}\right)$$

represents the same type of flow as in Problem 2.3, but with the strengths of source and sink now equal to $2\pi/h$. Show that, if the limit as $h \to 0$ is taken (in which process the strengths of source and sink are always inversely proportional to the distance between them), then the resulting flow is that arising from a doublet.

3 FLOW PAST AN OBSTACLE

After working through this section, you should be able to:

(a) explain the main features of the flow past a disc due to a uniform stream with circulation;

(b) explain what is meant by an *obstacle*, and state the *Obstacle Problem*;

(c) solve the Obstacle Problem in appropriate cases by applying the Flow Mapping Theorem, for flows with or without circulation around the obstacle;

(d) explain what is meant by a *Joukowski aerofoil.*

3.1 Flow past a circular cylinder

In this subsection we return to the flow considered in Frame 7 for which the model flow velocity function is

$$q(z) = 1 - a^2/\bar{z}^2 \qquad (z \in \mathbb{C} - \{0\}), \tag{3.1}$$

and a corresponding complex potential function is

$$\Omega(z) = z + a^2/z.$$

Indeed,

$$\overline{\Omega'(z)} = q(z).$$

Here, and throughout this section, the symbol a denotes a positive real number.

Problem 3.1 _____

(a) Verify that the points $z = a$ and $z = -a$ are the only stagnation points of the flow defined by Equation (3.1).

(b) Show that the flow defined by Equation (3.1) satisfies

$$q(ae^{it}) = (-2i \sin t)e^{it}, \qquad \text{for } 0 \le t \le 2\pi.$$

Hence derive the flow speed at the point $z = ae^{it}$, on the circle $\{z : |z| = a\}$.

Here the parameter t does not stand for time, as it did in Section 1.

In the audio tape (Frame 8) we claimed that Equation (3.1) can be used to describe the flow due to a uniform stream past a solid cylinder of circular cross-section (see Figure 3.1); we shall denote this cross-section as follows:

$$K_a = \{z : |z| \le a\}, \quad \text{where } a > 0. \tag{3.2}$$

This claim was based on the fact that $\partial K_a = \{z : |z| = a\}$ is made up of streamlines. However, there are other possible model flows for which ∂K_a is made up of streamlines. The complex potential function

$$\Omega(z) = -ic \operatorname{Log} z \qquad (z \in \mathbb{C}_\pi),$$

where $c \in \mathbb{R}$, corresponds to *vortex flow* (see Frame 4), and its streamlines are all circles with centre 0. Thus it seems reasonable to suppose that the complex potential function

$$\Omega_{a,c}(z) = z + \frac{a^2}{z} - ic \operatorname{Log} z \qquad (z \in \mathbb{C}_\pi) \tag{3.3}$$

should correspond to a model flow velocity function for which ∂K_a is made up of streamlines. This flow will play a major role in this unit and so we record its main properties in a theorem.

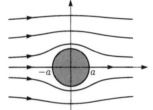

Figure 3.1

This complex potential is c times that for the vortex flow in Frame 4.

> **Theorem 3.1** For $a > 0$, $c \in \mathbb{R}$, the model flow velocity function
>
> $$q_{a,c}(z) = \overline{1 - \frac{a^2}{z^2} - \frac{ic}{z}} \qquad (z \in \mathbb{C} - \{0\}), \tag{3.4}$$
>
> corresponding to the complex potential function $\Omega_{a,c}$ of Equation (3.3), satisfies the following properties:
>
> (a) $\displaystyle\lim_{z \to \infty} q_{a,c}(z) = 1$;
>
> (b) ∂K_a is made up of streamlines for $q_{a,c}$;
>
> (c) for any simple-closed contour Γ surrounding K_a,
>
>   (i) $\displaystyle\mathcal{C}_\Gamma = \mathrm{Re} \int_\Gamma \overline{q_{a,c}}(z)\,dz = 2\pi c$,
>
>   and
>
>   (ii) $\displaystyle\mathcal{F}_\Gamma = \mathrm{Im} \int_\Gamma \overline{q_{a,c}}(z)\,dz = 0$.

Note that
$$\overline{\Omega'_{a,c}(z)} = q_{a,c}(z)$$
on $\mathbb{C}_\pi$, but $q_{a,c}$ has domain $\mathbb{C} - \{0\}$.

Remarks

1 The expression $\displaystyle\lim_{z \to \infty} q_{a,c}(z)$ is defined in a similar way to an ordinary limit as z tends to α, where $\alpha \in \mathbb{C}$; in particular, $\displaystyle\lim_{z \to \infty} q_{a,c}(z) = 1$ means that

    if $\{z_n\}$ is a sequence such that $z_n \to \infty$, then $q_{a,c}(z_n) \to 1$.

Unit A3, Section 3

2 Since $\mathcal{C}_\Gamma = 2\pi c$ for any simple-closed contour Γ surrounding K_a, we call $2\pi c$ the **circulation around the disc K_a**.

3 In fact it can be shown that Property (c)(ii) is a consequence of Property (b).

Proof of Theorem 3.1

Property (a) follows immediately from Equation (3.4). To verify Property (b), note that, for $z \in \partial K_a$, and $z \neq -a$, we have

$$\mathrm{Im}(\Omega_{a,c}(z)) = \mathrm{Im}\left(z + a^2/z\right) + \mathrm{Im}(-ic \,\mathrm{Log}\, z)$$
$$= -c \log_e a \qquad \text{(Frames 4 and 7)}.$$

Since $-c \log_e a$ is a constant, the set ∂K_a, is made up of streamlines for $q_{a,c}$. To verify Property (c), we use the Residue Theorem to obtain

$$\int_\Gamma \overline{q_{a,c}}(z)\,dz = \int_\Gamma \left(1 - \frac{a^2}{z^2} - \frac{ic}{z}\right) dz$$
$$= 2\pi i(-ic) = 2\pi c.$$

Hence $\mathcal{C}_\Gamma = 2\pi c$ and $\mathcal{F}_\Gamma = 0$. ∎

To include $z = -a$, we consider a logarithm function with a different cut, as discussed on the audio tape.

The additional vortex term (which gives rise to the non-zero circulation around Γ) affects the positions of the stagnation points, as we now ask you to verify.

The stagnation points for the case $c = 0$ were found in Problem 3.1.

Problem 3.2

It follows from Equation (3.4) that $q_{a,c}(z) = 0$ if and only if

$$z^2 - icz - a^2 = 0.$$

By solving this equation, find the stagnation points of the flow. Take c to be negative and describe the locations of these stagnation points when

(a) $-2a < c < 0$;   (b) $c = -2a$;   (c) $c < -2a$.

We ask you to concentrate on the cases with negative c because these will be particularly relevant later in the unit.

Theorem 3.1 allows us to think of $q_{a,c}$ as the model flow velocity function obtained by placing the 'obstacle' K_a into a uniform stream (for which $q(z) = 1$) and requiring that there is no flow of fluid across any segment of ∂K_a, but that the circulation of the flow around K_a is $2\pi c$.

Each streamline of this flow satisfies an equation of the form

$$\text{Im}(\Omega_{a,c}(z)) = \text{Im}(z + a^2/z) + \text{Im}(-ic\,\text{Log}\,z)$$
$$= y\left(1 - \frac{a^2}{x^2 + y^2}\right) - c\log_e(x^2 + y^2)^{1/2}$$
$$= \text{constant}.$$

Unfortunately it is not possible to solve these equations (for y in terms of x, or vice versa) when $c \neq 0$. The streamline diagrams (for various values of $c \leq 0$) in Figure 3.2 are based on computer plots. The directions of the arrows can be obtained from Equation (3.4); a quick method is to start with $q(z) \cong 1$ when $|z|$ is large, and then use continuity.

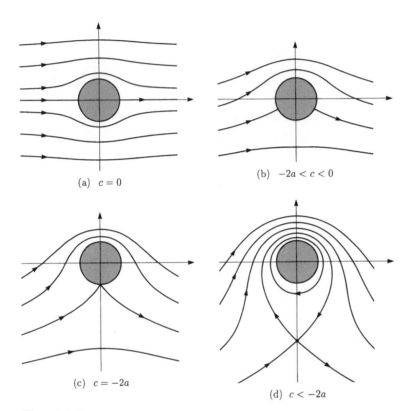

(a) $c = 0$

(b) $-2a < c < 0$

(c) $c = -2a$

(d) $c < -2a$

Figure 3.2

Figure 3.2(d) should be familiar — it is the cover design of Block D!

Notice how the shapes of these streamlines are closely related to the locations of the stagnation points in each case. For $c = 0$ (Figure 3.2(a)), the two stagnation points are symmetrically placed on the real axis at $z = \pm a$, by Problem 3.1. As c decreases from 0 to $-2a$, the two stagnation points (obtained in Problem 3.2)

$$z = \tfrac{1}{2}ic \pm \sqrt{a^2 - \tfrac{1}{4}c^2}$$

move round the circle $|z| = a$, remaining symmetric with respect to the imaginary axis (Figure 3.2(b)), until $c = -2a$, when they coalesce to form a single stagnation point at $z = -ia$ (Figure 3.2(c)). For $c < -2a$, the single stagnation point moves off the circle down the imaginary axis (Figure 3.2(d)) at

$$z = i\left(\tfrac{1}{2}c - \sqrt{\tfrac{1}{4}c^2 - a^2}\right).$$

A similar analysis can be carried out for positive values of c, resulting in streamline diagrams which are reflections in the real axis of the diagrams in Figure 3.2.

The other stagnation point lies inside the open disc $\{z : |z| < a\}$, as shown in the solution to Problem 3.2(c).

3.2 The Obstacle Problem

We now discuss the problem of determining the flow past a more general obstacle in a uniform stream. To begin with, we make precise what is meant here by an obstacle: this should be thought of as the two-dimensional cross-section of an object, extending indefinitely far perpendicular to the complex plane.

Definition An **obstacle** is a compact connected set K in $\mathbb{C}$, such that $\mathbb{C} - K$ is also connected.

The notions 'compact' and 'connected' were defined in *Unit A3*, Subsections 5.1 and 4.3, respectively.

Remark It follows that $\mathbb{C} - K$ is a region.

According to this definition, the closed disc $K_a = \{z : |z| \le a\}$ is an obstacle, as is the union of an ellipse with its inside, but the open disc $\{z : |z| < a\}$ is not an obstacle. Also the line segment joining α and β is an obstacle. Later in the unit this line segment is denoted by $L(\alpha, \beta)$; thus

$$L(\alpha, \beta) = \{(1-t)\alpha + t\beta : 0 \le t \le 1\}.$$

In particular, we shall consider the flow past line segments of the form $L(-\alpha, \alpha)$, whose centre is at 0.

Note that $L(\alpha, \beta)$ and $L(\beta, \alpha)$ describe the same line segment. Also, if α, β are both real, and $\alpha < \beta$, then $L(\alpha, \beta) = L(\beta, \alpha) = [\alpha, \beta]$.

The Obstacle Problem is to find, for a given obstacle K and a given $c \in \mathbb{R}$, a model flow velocity function which, loosely speaking, satisfies Properties (a), (b) and (c) of Theorem 3.1. Properties (a) and (c) are easy to state for a general obstacle, but Property (b) is more tricky. We want ∂K, the boundary of K, to look, as far as possible, as if it is made up of streamlines, but it is difficult to express this in terms of the velocity function q, because q may behave badly near some points, such as corners of ∂K. Instead we express this streamline condition in terms of a stream function, which is the imaginary part of a complex potential function Ω for q. As with the complex potential function $\Omega_{a,c}$, used in the proof of Theorem 3.1, we cannot expect that Ω will be analytic on the whole of $\mathbb{C} - K$, but we try to make its region of analyticity as large as possible, so that we can give meaning to the streamline condition

$\Omega_{a,c}$ is analytic on $(\mathbb{C} - K_a) - \{x \in \mathbb{R} : x < -a\}$, which is a subset of $\mathbb{C}_\pi$.

$$\text{Im}(\Omega(z)) = \text{constant}, \qquad \text{for } z \in \partial K,$$

even though ∂K may not be in the domain of Ω and q.

Obstacle Problem

Given an obstacle K and a real number c, we seek a model flow velocity function q with domain the region $\mathcal{R} = \mathbb{C} - K$, satisfying the following properties:

(a) $\lim\limits_{z \to \infty} q(z) = 1$;

(b) there is a complex potential function Ω for q on either $\mathcal{R}$ or $\mathcal{R} - \Sigma$, where Σ is a simple smooth path in $\mathcal{R}$, and a real constant k such that

for each $\alpha \in \partial K$, we have $\lim\limits_{z \to \alpha} \text{Im}(\Omega(z)) = k$;

(c) for any simple-closed contour Γ surrounding K,

$$\mathcal{C}_\Gamma = 2\pi c.$$

A **simple path** is one which does not intersect itself (see *Unit B2*, Subsection 1.1, where the domain of the parametrization of the path was assumed to be of the form $[a, b]$).

Remarks

1 Property (b) is illustrated in Figure 3.3 for the case where there is a complex potential Ω for q on $\mathcal{R} - \Sigma$.

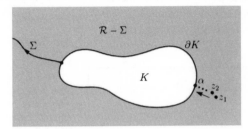

Figure 3.3

Recall that $\lim_{z \to \alpha} \mathrm{Im}(\Omega(z)) = k$ means that α is a limit point of $\mathcal{R} - \Sigma$ and, for each sequence $\{z_n\}$ in $\mathcal{R} - \Sigma$ such that $z_n \to \alpha$, we have $\mathrm{Im}(\Omega(z_n)) \to k$. Thus, in this case, Property (b) could be expressed, equivalently, by saying that the function $\mathrm{Im}\,\Omega$ has a continuous extension from $\mathcal{R} - \Sigma$ to $(\mathcal{R} - \Sigma) \cup \partial K$ with

$$\mathrm{Im}\,\Omega(z) = k, \qquad \text{for } z \in \partial K.$$

Unit A3, Section 3

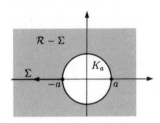

Figure 3.4

2 It is clear from the proof of Theorem 3.1 that the function $q_{a,c}$ in Equation (3.4) solves the Obstacle Problem for $K = K_a = \{z : |z| \le a\}$, with circulation $2\pi c$ around K. The simple smooth path Σ in Property (b) is the part of the negative real axis which lies in $\mathbb{C} - K_a$ (see Figure 3.4), and the constant k is $-c\log_e a$, as in the proof of Theorem 3.1. Note that if $c = 0$, then the simple smooth path Σ is not needed since the complex potential function $\Omega(z) = z + a^2/z$ is analytic on $\mathbb{C} - \{0\}$ and hence on $\mathbb{C} - K_a$.

3 Despite the comments before the statement of the Obstacle Problem, we *shall* refer to flow velocities on ∂K when it makes sense to do so. This will be the case when q has a continuous extension from $\mathbb{C} - K$ to ∂K (as does $q_{a,c}$ when $K = K_a$). When this notion is ambiguous (for example, when the obstacle is a line segment with different limiting velocities as it is approached from either side) we find it convenient to refer to velocities 'on either side of the boundary'. We consider such an example in Remark 2 after Example 3.1.

4 You will have noticed that Property (c) does not include the statement $\mathcal{F}_\Gamma = 0$. In fact, it is a consequence of Property (b) that $\mathcal{F}_\Gamma = 0$, so to add this to the *requirements* for q in the Obstacle Problem would be to introduce redundancy. In Theorem 3.1, the property $\mathcal{F}_\Gamma = 0$ is a consequence of the form of $q_{a,c}$ given in Equation (3.4), even though it can be deduced from Property (b).

5 The quantity $2\pi c$ in Property (c) is the **circulation around the obstacle** K.

In the next problem we ask you to verify that the velocity function $q(z) = 1$ solves the Obstacle Problem in a simple case with zero circulation (so that the simple smooth path Σ is not needed).

Problem 3.3

Show that the model flow velocity function

$$q(z) = 1$$

solves the Obstacle Problem for any line segment K parallel to the real axis, with zero circulation around K.

3.3 Flow Mapping Theorem

Problem 3.3 shows that the Obstacle Problem has a very simple solution for an obstacle K consisting of a line segment parallel to the real axis when the circulation around K is 0. However, if the line segment is not parallel to the real axis, or if the circulation is not 0, the Obstacle Problem becomes much harder to solve.

The velocity function $q(z) = 1$, which solved the Obstacle Problem in Problem 3.3, is one which you might have guessed. Rather than attempt to guess solutions to the Obstacle Problem for particular obstacles K and given circulations, we shall use a technique based on conformal mappings. The idea is that if K is a given obstacle and f is a suitable conformal mapping from $\mathbb{C} - K$ onto $\mathbb{C} - K_a$, where $K_a = \{z : |z| \le a\}$, then it is possible to use our solution $q_{a,c}$ of the Obstacle Problem for K_a in order to solve the Obstacle Problem for K. The details are given in the following result.

Theorem 3.2 Flow Mapping Theorem

Let K be an obstacle and let f be a one-one conformal mapping from $\mathbb{C} - K$ onto $\mathbb{C} - K_a$, where $a > 0$, such that

$$f(z) = z + a_0 + \frac{a_{-1}}{z} + \frac{a_{-2}}{z^2} + \cdots, \qquad \text{for } |z| > R, \qquad (3.5)$$

where $R > 0$ and $a_0, a_{-1}, a_{-2}, \ldots \in \mathbb{C}$. Then the velocity function

$$q(z) = q_{a,c}(f(z))\overline{f'(z)} \qquad (z \in \mathbb{C} - K) \qquad (3.6)$$

is the unique solution to the Obstacle Problem for K, with complex potential function

$$\Omega = \Omega_{a,c} \circ f.$$

The proof of this theorem is given at the end of this subsection.

K_a, $q_{a,c}$ and $\Omega_{a,c}$ are given in Equations (3.2), (3.4) and (3.3), respectively.

Remarks

1 Theorem 3.2 is illustrated in Figure 3.5, which also indicates that the conformal mapping f maps streamlines to streamlines. This is so because $\Omega = \Omega_{a,c} \circ f$ and so, for any constant k, the image under f of the set

$$\{z : \text{Im}(\Omega(z)) = k\} = \{z : \text{Im}(\Omega_{a,c}(f(z))) = k\}$$

is the set $\{w : \text{Im}(\Omega_{a,c}(w)) = k\}$.

Similarly the conformal mapping f^{-1} maps streamlines to streamlines.

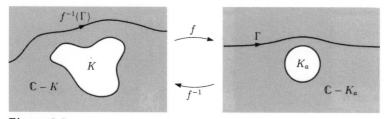

Figure 3.5

2 It follows from Equation (3.5), which gives the form of the Laurent series about 0 for f on $\{z : |z| > R\}$, that for large $|z|$, f behaves approximately like a translation. Hence, f cannot be a non-trivial rotation or a scaling.

Theorem 3.2 reduces the Obstacle Problem for K to the problem of finding a one-one conformal mapping from $\mathbb{C} - K$ onto $\mathbb{C} - K_a$, for some $a > 0$. In general, this is a hard problem, but there are some cases which can be solved explicitly. One simple example is the subject of Problem 3.4.

Problem 3.4

Use the Flow Mapping Theorem to solve the Obstacle Problem for the disc

$$K = \{z : |z - \beta| \le a\},$$

where β is any complex number and the circulation around the disc is $2\pi c$.

Another example employs the inverse function of the Joukowski function. In *Unit D1*, Subsection 4.4, you saw that the Joukowski function

$$J(z) = z + \frac{1}{z} \qquad (z \in \mathbb{C} - \{0\})$$

gives a one-one conformal mapping from $\mathbb{C} - K_1$, where $K_1 = \{z : |z| \le 1\}$, onto $\mathbb{C} - K$, where K is the line segment $L(-2, 2) = [-2, 2]$. Therefore J^{-1}, which is the inverse function of the restriction of J to $\mathbb{C} - K_1$, gives a one-one conformal mapping from $\mathbb{C} - K$ onto $\mathbb{C} - K_1$ (see Figure 3.6). The rule for J^{-1} was found to be

$$J^{-1}(w) = \tfrac{1}{2}\left(w + w\sqrt{1 - 4/w^2}\right).$$

Also, since

$$\partial K_1 = \{e^{it} : 0 \le t \le 2\pi\},$$

we have

$$J(\partial K_1) = \{e^{it} + 1/e^{it} : 0 \le t \le 2\pi\}$$
$$= \{2\cos t : 0 \le t \le 2\pi\} = [-2, 2].$$

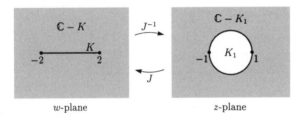

w-plane   z-plane

Figure 3.6

It follows that, if we reverse the roles of z and w here, then we can use J^{-1} as the function f in the Flow Mapping Theorem and so solve the Obstacle Problem for the line segment $K = [-2, 2]$ with *non-zero* circulation.

Example 3.1

Use the function J^{-1} to show that the solution to the Obstacle Problem for $K = [-2, 2]$ with circulation $2\pi c$ around K is

$$q(z) = 1 - \overline{\left(\frac{ic}{z\sqrt{1 - 4/z^2}}\right)}.$$

Solution

As pointed out above,

$$f(z) = J^{-1}(z) = \tfrac{1}{2}\left(z + z\sqrt{1 - 4/z^2}\right)$$

is a one-one conformal mapping from $\mathbb{C} - K$ onto $\mathbb{C} - K_1$, so that $a = 1$ in this case. To verify Condition (3.5), we need to express J^{-1} as a Laurent series about 0, valid on the exterior of some closed disc. To do this we use the binomial series

Unit B3, Theorem 3.2

$$\left(1 - 4/z^2\right)^{1/2} = 1 + \tfrac{1}{2}\left(-4/z^2\right) + \left(\tfrac{1}{2}\right)\left(-\tfrac{1}{2}\right)\frac{\left(-4/z^2\right)^2}{2!} + \cdots,$$

$$\text{for } |-4/z^2| < 1,$$

$$= 1 - \frac{2}{z^2} - \frac{2}{z^4} - \cdots, \qquad \text{for } |z| > 2,$$

and hence obtain

$$J^{-1}(z) = \tfrac{1}{2}\left(z + z\left(1 - \frac{2}{z^2} - \frac{2}{z^4} - \cdots\right)\right) = z - \frac{1}{z} - \frac{1}{z^3} - \cdots, \qquad \text{for } |z| > 2.$$

Thus J^{-1} is of the form given in Condition (3.5).

It follows, by the Flow Mapping Theorem with $a = 1$, that the velocity function

$$q(z) = q_{1,c}\big(J^{-1}(z)\big)\overline{(J^{-1})'(z)}$$

$$= \overline{\left(1 - \frac{1}{(J^{-1}(z))^2} - \frac{ic}{J^{-1}(z)}\right)}\,\overline{(J^{-1})'(z)}$$

solves the Obstacle Problem for K with circulation $2\pi c$ around K. To simplify this formula, we note that, by the Inverse Function Rule,

$$\left(J^{-1}\right)'(z) = \frac{1}{J'(J^{-1}(z))} = \frac{1}{1 - 1/(J^{-1}(z))^2},$$

and hence

$$q(z) = \overline{\left(1 - \frac{1}{(J^{-1}(z))^2} - \frac{ic}{J^{-1}(z)}\right)\left(1 - 1/(J^{-1}(z))^2\right)^{-1}}$$

$$= 1 - \overline{\left(\frac{ic}{J^{-1}(z) - 1/J^{-1}(z)}\right)}$$

$$= 1 - \overline{\left(\frac{ic}{2J^{-1}(z) - z}\right)}$$

$$= 1 - \overline{\left(\frac{ic}{z\sqrt{1 - 4/z^2}}\right)},$$

as required. ∎

$$J(w) = w + 1/w$$
$$\Longrightarrow$$
$$J'(w) = 1 - 1/w^2.$$

$$w = J^{-1}(z)$$
$$\Longrightarrow$$
$$z = J(w)$$
$$= w + \frac{1}{w}$$
$$= J^{-1}(z) + 1/J^{-1}(z).$$

Remarks

1 Notice that if $c = 0$ in Example 3.1, then we obtain the expected solution $q(z) = 1$, given in Problem 3.3.

2 Note that we can compute the velocities on either side of the obstacle $K = [-2, 2]$, by putting $z = x + iy$ in the expression for $q(z)$ and letting y tend to 0 through positive values (written $y \to 0^+$) and through negative values (written $y \to 0^-$).

For example, put $x = 0$, so that $z = iy$. Then

$$z\sqrt{1 - 4/z^2} = \begin{cases} i|y|\sqrt{1 - 4/(-y^2)}, & \text{for } y > 0, \\ -i|y|\sqrt{1 - 4/(-y^2)}, & \text{for } y < 0, \end{cases}$$

$$= \begin{cases} i\sqrt{y^2 + 4}, & \text{for } y > 0, \\ -i\sqrt{y^2 + 4}, & \text{for } y < 0, \end{cases}$$

$$\to \begin{cases} 2i & \text{as } y \to 0^+, \\ -2i & \text{as } y \to 0^-. \end{cases}$$

Thus

$$q(iy) = 1 - \overline{\left(\frac{ic}{z\sqrt{1 - 4/z^2}}\right)}$$

$$\to \begin{cases} 1 - \tfrac{1}{2}c & \text{as } y \to 0^+, \\ 1 + \tfrac{1}{2}c & \text{as } y \to 0^-. \end{cases}$$

This suggests that negative circulation reinforces the flow above the obstacle and opposes it below.

3 An alternative method of obtaining the velocity function in Example 3.1 is first to determine the complex potential function $\Omega = \Omega_{a,c} \circ f$ (given by Theorem 3.2), differentiate Ω and then take its conjugate to give the rule for $q = \overline{\Omega'}$. We ask you to carry out this approach in the next problem.

Problem 3.5

Solve the Obstacle Problem for $K = [-2, 2]$, with circulation $2\pi c$ around K, by first showing that a complex potential function for the solution is

$$\Omega(z) = z - ic\,\mathrm{Log}\left(\tfrac{1}{2}(z + z\sqrt{1 - 4/z^2})\right).$$

(*Hint*:   The identity $\Omega_{1,c} = J - ic\,\mathrm{Log}$ will help.)

Note that if $c = 0$ then $\Omega(z) = z$. This happens because

$$\Omega_{1,0}(z) = z + \frac{1}{z} = J(z)$$

and

$$f(z) = J^{-1}(z).$$

The complex potential function Ω found in Problem 3.5 should, in principle, enable us to plot the streamlines for the corresponding flow round $K = [-2, 2]$, since these have equations of the form

$$\mathrm{Im}(\Omega(z)) = \text{constant}.$$

However, if $c \neq 0$, then this equation is so complicated that the streamlines can only be plotted accurately with the help of a computer.

An alternative approach to *sketching* these streamlines is to use the fact that the conformal mappings f and f^{-1} map streamlines to streamlines (see Remark 1 after the Flow Mapping Theorem). Thus, if Γ is any streamline for the velocity function $q_{1,c}$, then $f^{-1}(\Gamma)$ is a streamline for the velocity function q. We can therefore use the function $f^{-1} = J$ to transfer the appropriate streamline diagram in Figure 3.2 (where we had $c < 0$) from $\mathbb{C} - K_1$ to $\mathbb{C} - K$. Of course, you can only hope to do this approximately by hand, but some precision can be achieved if you first calculate the effect that $f^{-1} = J$ has on the stagnation points of the flow with velocity function $q_{1,c}$ (which were found in Problem 3.2). Since $a = 1$ in this case, the stagnation points are

$$w = \tfrac{1}{2}ic \pm \sqrt{1 - \tfrac{1}{4}c^2}, \qquad \text{if } -2 < c < 0, \tag{3.7}$$

and the single point

$$w = i\left(\tfrac{1}{2}c - \sqrt{\tfrac{1}{4}c^2 - 1}\right), \qquad \text{if } c \leq -2.$$

To illustrate the procedure we consider the case $-2 < c < 0$, for which the stagnation points lie on the boundary $\partial K_1 = \{w : |w| = 1\}$ of K_1. The function $f^{-1} = J$ is one-one and conformal on the region $\mathbb{C} - K_1$, but it can be extended to ∂K_1 by using the rule $J(w) = w + 1/w$ there.

It can be shown that J maps both the upper half and the lower half of ∂K_1 onto $K = [-2, 2]$, and so the restriction of J to ∂K_1 is not one-one. Also, it can be shown that J maps points in $\mathbb{C} - K_1$ near the upper half of ∂K_1 to points just above K and points in $\mathbb{C} - K_1$ near the lower half of ∂K_1 to points just below K (see Figure 3.7).

The material from here up to and including Figure 3.8 may be omitted on a first reading.

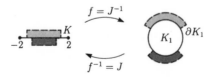

Figure 3.7

Since the stagnation points given by Equation (3.7) lie on the lower half of ∂K_1, the streamlines of the flow which end at these two stationary points are mapped by $f^{-1} = J$ to streamlines of the flow with velocity function q which approach $K = [-2, 2]$ from below, ending at the points $J\left(\tfrac{1}{2}ic \pm \sqrt{1 - \tfrac{1}{4}c^2}\right)$.

Once these points have been determined, we can sketch the corresponding streamlines (and others) by using the fact that

$$q(z) \cong 1, \qquad \text{for } |z| \text{ large,}$$

together with the symmetry of the streamlines with respect to the imaginary axis, which follows from the corresponding symmetry of the streamlines in Figure 3.2(b) and that of the obstacle K. A resulting sketch (for $c = -\sqrt{3}$) is shown in Figure 3.8. (The streamlines corresponding to other obstacles K may be sketched in a similar way.)

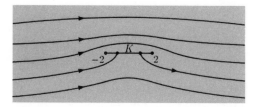

Figure 3.8

To increase the range of obstacles which we can deal with, we now introduce the family of mapping functions

$$J_a(z) = z + \frac{a^2}{z} \qquad (z \in \mathbb{C} - \{0\}),$$

Note that
$$\Omega_{a,c} = J_a - ic \operatorname{Log}.$$

where $a > 0$. These functions are closely related to the Joukowski function $J = J_1$, and we can deduce their basic properties by observing that

$$J_a(z) = a\left(z/a + \frac{1}{z/a} \right);$$

that is, $w = J_a(z)$ is obtained by composing
(a) the scaling $z_1 = z/a$;
(b) the Joukowski function $z_2 = J(z_1) = z_1 + 1/z_1$;
(c) the scaling $w = az_2$.

Problem 3.6

(a) Show that J_a is a one-one conformal mapping from $\mathbb{C} - K_a$ onto $\mathbb{C} - [-2a, 2a]$, and that J_a maps ∂K_a onto $[-2a, 2a]$.
(b) Verify that the inverse function J_a^{-1} of the restriction of J_a to $\mathbb{C} - K_a$ is

$$J_a^{-1}(w) = \tfrac{1}{2}\left(w + w\sqrt{1 - 4a^2/w^2} \right) \qquad (w \in \mathbb{C} - [-2a, 2a]).$$

The results of Problem 3.6 show that, if we reverse the roles of z and w, then we can use J_a^{-1} as the function f in the Flow Mapping Theorem to solve the Obstacle Problem for $K = [-2a, 2a]$, where $a > 0$.

Problem 3.7

Use the function J_a^{-1} to show that the solution to the Obstacle Problem for $K = [-2a, 2a]$ with circulation $2\pi c$ around K is

Note that Problem 3.7 generalizes Example 3.1.

$$q(z) = 1 - \overline{\left(\frac{ic}{z\sqrt{1 - 4a^2/z^2}} \right)}.$$

The functions J_a can also be used to solve the Obstacle Problem for flow around various other obstacles, such as an ellipse.

Problem 3.8

(a) Show that if $r > a$, then J_a maps the circle $C_r = \{w : |w| = r\}$ onto the ellipse in the z-plane shown in Figure 3.9.

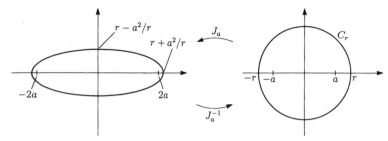

Figure 3.9

(b) Deduce from part (a) that the solution to the Obstacle Problem for the obstacle K comprising the ellipse in part (a) together with its inside, with circulation $2\pi c$ around K, is

$$q(z) = 1 - \overline{\left(\frac{r^2 - a^2 + icJ_a^{-1}(z)}{\left(J_a^{-1}(z)\right)^2 - a^2} \right)},$$

where $J_a^{-1}(z) = \frac{1}{2}\left(z + z\sqrt{1 - 4a^2/z^2}\right)$.

(*Hint:* Use the solution to Problem 3.7 when establishing Condition (3.5).)

We end this subsection with a proof of the Flow Mapping Theorem.

This proof may be omitted on a first reading.

Theorem 3.2 Flow Mapping Theorem

Let K be an obstacle and let f be a one-one conformal mapping from $\mathbb{C} - K$ onto $\mathbb{C} - K_a$, where $a > 0$, such that

$$f(z) = z + a_0 + \frac{a_{-1}}{z} + \frac{a_{-2}}{z^2} + \cdots, \qquad \text{for } |z| > R, \qquad (3.5)$$

where $R > 0$ and $a_0, a_{-1}, a_{-2}, \ldots \in \mathbb{C}$. Then the velocity function

$$q(z) = q_{a,c}(f(z))\overline{f'(z)} \qquad (z \in \mathbb{C} - K) \qquad (3.6)$$

is the unique solution to the Obstacle Problem for K, with complex potential function

$$\Omega = \Omega_{a,c} \circ f.$$

Proof Before verifying Properties (a), (b) and (c) of the Obstacle Problem, we observe that

We omit the proof of the uniqueness of the solution q.

$$q(z) = q_{a,c}(f(z))\overline{f'(z)}$$

$$= \overline{\left(1 - \frac{a^2}{(f(z))^2} - \frac{ic}{f(z)}\right)f'(z)}$$

is a model flow velocity function on $\mathcal{R} = \mathbb{C} - K$, since it is the conjugate of an analytic function there.

Now, using the Laurent series (3.5), we have

$$\lim_{z \to \infty} \frac{f(z)}{z} = 1 \qquad \text{and} \qquad \lim_{z \to \infty} f'(z) = 1.$$

Note that the functions

$$z \longmapsto f(z)/z$$

and f' both have removable singularities at ∞; see *Unit D1*, Section 1.

It follows that

$$\lim_{z\to\infty} q(z) = \lim_{z\to\infty} \overline{\left(1 - \frac{a^2}{(f(z))^2} - \frac{ic}{f(z)}\right) f'(z)}$$

$$= \lim_{z\to\infty} \overline{\left(1 - \frac{a^2}{z^2} - \frac{ic}{z}\right)} = 1,$$

which verifies Property (a) of the Obstacle Problem.

To verify Property (b) of the Obstacle Problem, we use the fact that f is one-one and analytic on $\mathcal{R}$ so that, by the Inverse Function Rule, f has an inverse function f^{-1} which is analytic on $\mathbb{C} - K_a$. Since $\Omega_{a,c}$ is analytic on $\mathbb{C}_\pi$, it follows that the composite function $\Omega_{a,c} \circ f$ is analytic on the region

$$f^{-1}(\mathbb{C}_\pi - K_a) = \mathcal{R} - f^{-1}(\Sigma_a),$$

where $\Sigma_a = \{u \in \mathbb{R} : u < -a\}$ is that part of the negative real axis in $\mathbb{C} - K_a$ (see Figure 3.10).

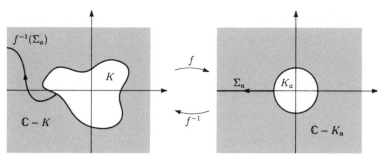

Figure 3.10

Since Σ_a is a simple smooth path and f^{-1} is one-one and analytic, it follows that $\Sigma = f^{-1}(\Sigma_a)$ is also a simple smooth path. Moreover $\Omega = \Omega_{a,c} \circ f$ is a complex potential function for q on $\mathcal{R} - \Sigma$, because

$$\overline{\Omega'(z)} = \overline{\Omega'_{a,c}(f(z)) f'(z)} \qquad \text{(Chain Rule)}$$

$$= \overline{\left(1 - \frac{a^2}{(f(z))^2} - \frac{ic}{f(z)}\right) f'(z)}$$

$$= q(z), \qquad \text{for } z \in \mathcal{R} - \Sigma.$$

To complete the verification of Property (b), we need to show that there is a constant k such that

$$\text{for each } \alpha \in \partial K, \text{ we have } \lim_{z\to\alpha} \text{Im}(\Omega(z)) = k. \tag{3.8}$$

To do this, first note that if $\alpha \in \partial K$, then α is a limit point of $\mathcal{R} - \Sigma$; indeed, each open disc with centre α must contain a point of $\mathcal{R} - \Sigma$ (because $\alpha \in \partial \mathcal{R}$ and Σ cannot fill up an open set) and so we can construct a sequence $\{z_n\}$ in $\mathcal{R} - \Sigma$ such that $z_n \to \alpha$.

Now suppose that $\{z_n\}$ lies in $\mathcal{R} - \Sigma$ and $z_n \to \alpha$. Then the sequence $\{w_n\} = \{f(z_n)\}$ lies in $\mathbb{C}_\pi - K_a$, and we claim that $|w_n| \to a$. Indeed, if $\varepsilon > 0$ is given and $\Gamma_\varepsilon = \{w : |w| = a + \varepsilon\}$, then $f^{-1}(\Gamma_\varepsilon)$ is a simple-closed contour in $\mathcal{R}$ which surrounds, but does not meet K (see Figure 3.11). Moreover, f^{-1} maps the outside of Γ_ε onto the outside of $f^{-1}(\Gamma_\varepsilon)$. It follows that the terms of $\{z_n\}$ must eventually lie inside $f^{-1}(\Gamma_\varepsilon)$, and hence that the terms of $\{w_n\}$ must eventually lie between Γ_ε and ∂K_a. Hence $|w_n| \to a$ as $n \to \infty$.

These plausible assertions can be verified by using the Argument Principle (*Unit C2*, Theorem 2.2), together with the fact that f is a one-one analytic function of the form given by Equation (3.5). We omit the details.

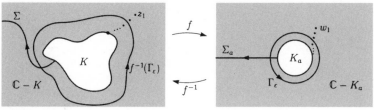

Figure 3.11

Therefore, if $w_n = u_n + iv_n$, for $n = 1, 2, \ldots$, then we have

$$\begin{aligned}
\mathrm{Im}(\Omega(z_n)) &= \mathrm{Im}(\Omega_{a,c}(f(z_n))) \\
&= \mathrm{Im}(\Omega_{a,c}(w_n)) \\
&= v_n\left(1 - \frac{a^2}{|w_n|^2}\right) - c\log_e |w_n| \qquad \text{(by Equation (3.3))} \\
&\to -c\log_e a \qquad \text{as } n \to \infty.
\end{aligned}$$

Thus Condition (3.8) holds with $k = -c\log_e a$.

Finally, we check Property (c). If Γ is any simple-closed contour surrounding K, then $f(\Gamma)$ is a simple-closed contour surrounding K_a and so

$$\begin{aligned}
\mathcal{C}_\Gamma + i\mathcal{F}_\Gamma &= \int_\Gamma \overline{q}(z)\, dz \\
&= \int_\Gamma \overline{q_{a,c}(f(z))} f'(z)\, dz \\
&= \int_{f(\Gamma)} \overline{q_{a,c}(w)}\, dw = 2\pi c \qquad \text{(by Theorem 3.1(c))}.
\end{aligned}$$

The substitution
$$w = f(z), \quad dw = f'(z)\, dz$$
can be justified as in the proof of the Argument Principle.

Note that this integral also gives $\mathcal{F}_\Gamma = 0$.

Hence $\mathcal{C}_\Gamma = 2\pi c$, as required. ∎

3.4 Aerofoils

You saw in Problem 3.6(a) that the analytic function $J_a(w) = w + a^2/w$ maps the circle $C_a = \{w : |w| = a\}$ to the line segment $[-2a, 2a]$, as well as being a one-one mapping of the region exterior to C_a onto $\mathbb{C} - [-2a, 2a]$. We consider next why the image under J_a of the smooth path C_a is 'pointed' (non-smooth) at both ends. This leads on to the definition of a type of *aerofoil*, which is a shape pointed at just one end.

As shown in *Unit A4*, if f is an analytic function and α is a point of its domain at which $f'(\alpha) \neq 0$, then f is conformal at α, which means that f preserves the angle between two smooth paths which meet at α. However, if α is a point for which $f'(\alpha) = 0$ but $f''(\alpha) \neq 0$, then the effect of f is to *double* the angle between two smooth paths emerging from α. (For a justification of this statement, see the Local Mapping Theorem (*Unit C2*, Theorem 3.2), and the Remark following its proof in Subsection 3.3, taking $n = 2$.) We call a point α at which the analytic function f has zero derivative a **critical point** of f.

Unit A4, Theorem 4.2

This explains why $J_a(C_a) = [-2a, 2a]$ is 'pointed' at both ends. For

$$J_a'(w) = 1 - \frac{a^2}{w^2}$$

is zero at $w = \pm a$, but $J_a''(\pm a) \neq 0$. The image points of $w = \pm a$ under J_a are at $z = \pm 2a$. The circle C_a may be thought of as a pair of smooth paths meeting at the points $w = \pm a$, with an angle π between them. The images of these two paths therefore meet at an angle 2π, producing the pointedness of the image contour. The image of any smooth path passing through $w = \pm a$ has a similar pointed nature.

Figure 3.12 illustrates two of the results obtained so far. The function $J_a(w) = w + a^2/w$ maps

Problems 3.6(a) and 3.8(a)

(a) the circle $C_a = \{w : |w| = a\}$ to the line segment $[-2a, 2a]$;

(b) the circle $C_r = \{w : |w| = r\}$, where $r > a$, to the ellipse

$$\left\{ x + iy : \frac{x^2}{(r + a^2/r)^2} + \frac{y^2}{(r - a^2/r)^2} = 1 \right\}.$$

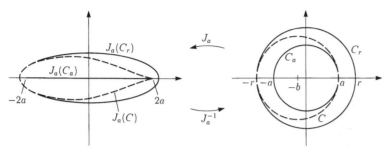

Figure 3.12

Consider now the circle

$$C = \{w : |w + b| = a + b\},$$

where $b = \frac{1}{2}(r - a)$. This circle, which is also shown in Figure 3.12, has the same tangent as the circle C_a at $w = a$, so that its image $J_a(C)$ can be expected to resemble that of $J_a(C_a) = [-2a, 2a]$ in the vicinity of $z = 2a$. In particular, $J_a(C)$ should be 'pointed' at $z = 2a$. The circle C has the same tangent as the circle C_r at $w = -r$, so that its image $J_a(C)$ can be expected to resemble that of the ellipse $J_a(C_r)$ in the vicinity of $z = -r - a^2/r$.

At all points of C other than $w = a$ we have $J_a'(w) \neq 0$, so the image contour is smooth except at the single point $z = 2a$. Also, the mapping J_a preserves the symmetry of C about the real axis, since $J_a(\overline{w}) = \overline{J_a(w)}$.

These considerations lead to the sketch of $J_a(C)$ shown in the z-plane on the left of Figure 3.12, and repeated in Figure 3.13.

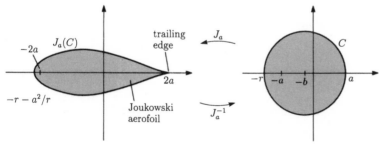

Figure 3.13

The obstacle with boundary $J_a(C)$ is called a *Joukowski aerofoil*. Note that the circle C which defines it passes through the critical point $w = a$ of J_a, whereas it surrounds the other critical point $w = -a$.

Definition A **Joukowski aerofoil** is an obstacle which (possibly after an appropriate translation or rotation) has boundary $J_a(B)$, where B is a circle which passes through the critical point $w = a$ of J_a, and surrounds the other critical point $w = -a$.

The point $z = 2a$ is called the **trailing edge** of the aerofoil.

In order for a Joukowski aerofoil to be symmetric, the centre of the circle C must lie on the (negative) real axis, as in Figure 3.13. Otherwise, the resulting aerofoil is asymmetric.

Remark The boundary $J_a(B)$ is smooth except at $z = 2a$, and surrounds the point $z = -2a$.

Problem 3.9

(a) Suppose that C is the circle $\{w : |w + b| = a + b\}$ (where $a, b > 0$), and that K is the Joukowski aerofoil for which $\partial K = J_a(C)$. Show that the solution to the Obstacle Problem for K with circulation $2\pi c$ around K corresponds to the complex potential function

$$\Omega(z) = w + b + \frac{(a + b)^2}{w + b} - ic \, \mathrm{Log}(w + b),$$

where $w = J_a^{-1}(z)$.

(b) Determine, in terms of w, the flow velocity function q for this flow, and show that $\lim_{z \to 2a} q(z)$ (the limiting velocity at the trailing edge) exists if and only if $c = 0$.

Apart from a case involving translation (Problem 3.4), we have so far considered only examples of obstacles which are symmetric about the real axis. While an aeroplane is in flight, the wing cross-section is at a slight angle to the oncoming airstream. We may model this situation by placing a symmetric Joukowski aerofoil at an angle ϕ to a uniform stream, and attempt to find a complex potential for this version of the Obstacle Problem (see Figure 3.14). In these circumstances, ϕ is known as the aerofoil's **angle of attack**.

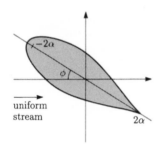

Figure 3.14

In order to make progress here, we shall extend the family of mapping functions J_a. The extension required is to allow the parameter a to become complex, that is, to consider the family of mapping functions

$$J_\alpha(w) = w + \frac{\alpha^2}{w}, \tag{3.9}$$

where α is any non-zero complex number. Note that if $\phi = -\operatorname{Arg}\alpha$, then Equation (3.9) can be written as

In other words, we have
$$\alpha = |\alpha| e^{-i\phi},$$
where $-\pi \le \phi < \pi$.

$$J_\alpha(w) = e^{-i\phi}\left(we^{i\phi} + \frac{|\alpha|^2}{we^{i\phi}}\right),$$

showing that the transformation $z = J_\alpha(w)$ is a composition of the three transformations

(a) $w_1 = we^{i\phi}$ (an anticlockwise rotation through the angle ϕ);

(b) $w_2 = J_{|\alpha|}(w_1) = w_1 + |\alpha|^2/w_1$ (a mapping of the type J_a, with $a = |\alpha|$);

(c) $z = w_2 e^{-i\phi}$ (a clockwise rotation through the angle ϕ).

Thus, if we denote by R_ϕ the anticlockwise rotation of $\mathbb{C}$ about 0 through the angle ϕ, then

$$J_\alpha = R_\phi^{-1} \circ J_{|\alpha|} \circ R_\phi. \tag{3.10}$$

Suppose that $K_{|\alpha|}$ is the closed disc $\{w : |w| \le |\alpha|\}$, whose boundary $C_{|\alpha|} = \partial K_{|\alpha|}$ includes the point α. Figure 3.15 shows, using the decomposition of Equation (3.10), that J_α maps $\mathbb{C} - K_{|\alpha|}$ onto $\mathbb{C} - L(-2\alpha, 2\alpha)$, as well as mapping $C_{|\alpha|}$ to $L(-2\alpha, 2\alpha)$.

$L(-2\alpha, 2\alpha)$ denotes the line segment joining -2α and 2α.

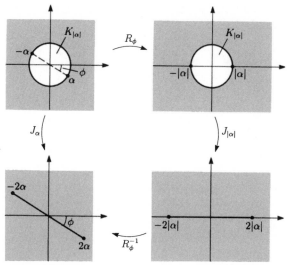

Figure 3.15

Since each of the constituent mappings is one-one on the appropriate region, the mapping J_α restricted to $\mathbb{C} - K_{|\alpha|}$ is also one-one. This restriction of J_α therefore has an inverse function J_α^{-1}, which is a one-one conformal mapping from $\mathbb{C} - L(-2\alpha, 2\alpha)$ onto $\mathbb{C} - K_{|\alpha|}$. From Equation (3.10), we have

$$J_\alpha^{-1} = \left(R_\phi^{-1} \circ J_{|\alpha|} \circ R_\phi \right)^{-1}$$

$$= R_\phi^{-1} \circ J_{|\alpha|}^{-1} \circ R_\phi.$$

Using the formula for $J_a^{-1}(z)$ (see Problem 3.6(b)), with $a = |\alpha|$, we deduce that

$$J_\alpha^{-1}(z) = e^{-i\phi} \frac{e^{i\phi}}{2} \left(z + z\sqrt{1 - \frac{4|\alpha|^2}{(ze^{i\phi})^2}} \right);$$

that is,

$$J_\alpha^{-1}(z) = \tfrac{1}{2}\left(z + z\sqrt{1 - 4\alpha^2/z^2} \right) \qquad (z \in \mathbb{C} - L(-2\alpha, 2\alpha)), \qquad (3.11)$$

as expected in view of the formula for J_a^{-1}.

Example 3.2

(a) Find a complex potential which provides a solution to the Obstacle Problem when the obstacle K is the line segment $L(-2\alpha, 2\alpha)$ and the circulation around K is $2\pi c$.

(b) Verify, from your answer to part (a) with $c = 0$, that the circulation-free complex potential for $\alpha = a$ (where a is real) is $\Omega(z) = z$, as expected.

(c) Determine the velocity function q which solves the Obstacle Problem for $K = L(-ai, ai)$, with zero circulation.

Here K may be regarded as a thin plate of height $2a$ placed at right angles to a uniform flow.

Solution

(a) As shown above, J_α^{-1} is a one-one conformal mapping from $\mathbb{C} - L(-2\alpha, 2\alpha)$ onto $\mathbb{C} - K_{|\alpha|}$. Also, it can be shown that the function $f = J_\alpha^{-1}$ satisfies Condition (3.5) of the Flow Mapping Theorem. The appropriate Laurent series is obtained as in Problem 3.7, with α in place of a. A suitable complex potential for the flow past K, with circulation $2\pi c$ around K, is

$$\Omega(z) = \left(\Omega_{|\alpha|,c} \circ J_\alpha^{-1} \right)(z)$$

$$= J_\alpha^{-1}(z) + \frac{|\alpha|^2}{J_\alpha^{-1}(z)} - ic\,\mathrm{Log}\left(J_\alpha^{-1}(z) \right)$$

$$= z + \frac{|\alpha|^2 - \alpha^2}{J_\alpha^{-1}(z)} - ic\,\mathrm{Log}\left(J_\alpha^{-1}(z) \right),$$

since $J_\alpha^{-1}(z) + \dfrac{\alpha^2}{J_\alpha^{-1}(z)} = z$.

(b) With $c = 0$, we have

$$\Omega(z) = z + \frac{|\alpha|^2 - \alpha^2}{J_\alpha^{-1}(z)},$$

so that if $\alpha = a$, where a is real, then the complex potential is

$$\Omega(z) = z,$$

as in the solution to Problem 3.3.

(c) If $c = 0$ and $\alpha = \frac{1}{2}ai$, then we find from part (a) that

$$\Omega(z) = z + \frac{\frac{1}{2}a^2}{\frac{1}{2}z\left(1 + \sqrt{1 + a^2/z^2}\right)}$$

$$= z + \frac{a^2\left(1 - \sqrt{1 + a^2/z^2}\right)}{z\left(1 + \sqrt{1 + a^2/z^2}\right)\left(1 - \sqrt{1 + a^2/z^2}\right)}$$

$$= z + \frac{a^2\left(1 - \sqrt{1 + a^2/z^2}\right)}{-a^2/z} = z\sqrt{1 + \frac{a^2}{z^2}}.$$

The required flow velocity function is therefore

$$q(z) = \overline{\Omega'(z)}$$

$$= \overline{\sqrt{1 + \frac{a^2}{z^2}} + z \cdot \frac{1}{2}\frac{1}{\sqrt{1 + a^2/z^2}} \cdot \frac{-2a^2}{z^3}}$$

$$= \overline{\sqrt{1 + \frac{a^2}{z^2} - \frac{a^2}{z^2}\frac{1}{\sqrt{1 + a^2/z^2}}}}$$

$$= \overline{1/\sqrt{1 + a^2/z^2}}. \quad\blacksquare$$

Note that q is unbounded near $\pm ai$, the ends of the line segment.

Remark In part (c), the velocity function q could have been obtained directly from Equation (3.6), as we did in the solution to Example 3.1.

To end the section, we ask you to solve the Obstacle Problem for a rotated aerofoil.

Problem 3.10

(a) Suppose that the Joukowski aerofoil K shown in Figure 3.14 is obtained by rotating the aerofoil in Figure 3.13 and Problem 3.9 clockwise about the origin through an angle ϕ. We then have

$$\partial K = \left(R_\phi^{-1} \circ J_a\right)(C),$$

where, as before, C is the circle $\{w : |w + b| = a + b\}$. With $\alpha = ae^{-i\phi}$, use Equation (3.10) to show that the aerofoil boundary ∂K is the image under J_α of the circle

$$R_\phi^{-1}(C) = \left\{w : |w + be^{-i\phi}| = a + b\right\},$$

as shown in Figure 3.16.

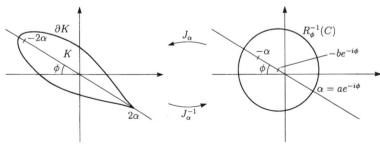

Figure 3.16

(b) Determine a complex potential which provides a solution to the Obstacle Problem when the obstacle K is the Joukowski aerofoil of part (a), at angle ϕ to the incoming stream, with circulation $2\pi c$ around K.

(c) Determine the corresponding flow velocity function q, in terms of $w = J_\alpha^{-1}(z)$, and show that $\lim\limits_{z \to 2\alpha} q(z)$ (the limiting velocity at the trailing edge) exists if and only if

$$c = -2(a + b)\sin\phi.$$

(*Hint*: In order to make the algebra more manageable, use the auxiliary variables

$$w_1 = w - \alpha = w - ae^{-i\phi},$$
$$w_2 = w + be^{-i\phi} = w_1 + (a + b)e^{-i\phi},$$

and note that $w_1 \to 0$ as $z \to 2\alpha$.)

The consideration of aerofoils is followed up in the next section, where we develop our model further in order to calculate the *force* acting on an obstacle, due to the fluid streaming past it. You will see that the *circulation* around the obstacle is of primary importance in this context and, as far as aerofoils are concerned, the solution to Problem 3.10(c) will play a key role.

4 LIFT AND DRAG

After working through this section, you should be able to:

(a) explain the meaning of Bernoulli's Equation, and apply it to find the *pressure distribution* of a model fluid flow;

(b) find the *total force* acting on an obstacle due to a model fluid flow, either directly from the pressure distribution, or by the application of Blasius' Theorem, or by using the Kutta–Joukowski Lift Theorem;

(c) understand why the Kutta–Joukowski Hypothesis leads to a bounded velocity function for flow past a Joukowski aerofoil, and a unique value for the force on the aerofoil.

4.1 Bernoulli's Equation

Our aim in this section is to investigate the *force* acting on an obstacle located in a fluid flow, using the velocity functions found in various cases in Section 3. This force is caused by the fluid pressure on the boundary of the obstacle, and its value may be obtained by calculating a suitable contour integral.

Pressure is a scalar quantity (that is, it has magnitude but no associated direction), which may be modelled within the flow region by a non-negative real-valued function p. This function is called the pressure *distribution* within the fluid. It is defined to be the *magnitude of the force per unit area* acting within the fluid. This means that, on any small area δA of a fixed surface which includes z, the pressure gives rise to a force of approximate magnitude $p(z)\delta A$, in the direction perpendicular to the surface at z (see Figure 4.1).

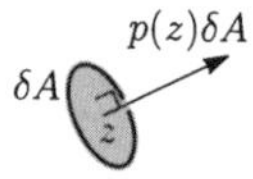

We now relate the pressure $p(z)$ of the fluid at the point z to its velocity $q(z)$. A convenient modelling link is provided by the equation below.

> ### Bernoulli's Equation
>
> In a fluid of constant density ρ, the relationship between the fluid pressure $p(z)$ and the fluid speed $|q(z)|$, at the point z, is given by **Bernoulli's Equation**
>
> $$p(z) + \tfrac{1}{2}\rho|q(z)|^2 = p_0, \tag{4.1}$$
>
> where p_0 is a constant.

Remarks

1 A derivation of Bernoulli's Equation is given in Subsection 4.4. It is an integral version of Newton's Second Law (force = mass × acceleration) applied to a small volume of fluid, and is the counterpart of an energy equation in single-particle mechanics. Its derivation assumes that all forces acting within the fluid other than those due to the pressure may be ignored. In particular, gravitational and viscous effects are ignored.

2 The constant p_0 is the fluid pressure at any stagnation point, as can be seen by putting $q(z) = 0$ in Bernoulli's Equation. For a flow satisfying the Obstacle Problem, p_0 can be expressed in terms of p_∞, the pressure at large distances from the obstacle. Since $\lim_{z \to \infty} q(z) = 1$, we have

$$p_0 = p_\infty + \tfrac{1}{2}\rho.$$

3 In words, Bernoulli's Equation says that *a pressure increase is accompanied by a decrease in the fluid speed*, and vice versa.

Force is a vector quantity.

The pressure on the surface of a solid object in contact with a fluid is associated with momentum changes brought about by large numbers of fluid molecules 'bouncing off' the molecules in the solid surface. This explanation lies outside our continuum model for the fluid.

Figure 4.1

Daniel Bernoulli (1700–82) came from a Swiss family which yielded famous mathematicians throughout the eighteenth century. He was in succession Professor of Medicine, Metaphysics and Natural Philosophy at the University of Basle. The word 'hydrodynamics' originated from his publication of *Hydrodynamica* in 1738, which was the first substantial work in the theory of fluid motion.

Viscous effects are caused by the internal friction of a fluid. We say more about this in Subsection 4.3.

The prediction in Remark 3 may be used in circumstances which go beyond our current two-dimensional model. For example, if you hold two sheets of paper vertically, a few centimetres apart, and blow between them, you will find that the sheets tend to move together (see Figure 4.2). The explanation is as follows.

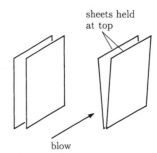

sheets held at top

blow

Figure 4.2

The blowing between the paper sheets produces a higher flow velocity in the region between them than outside. Bernoulli's Equation predicts that the pressure between the sheets will therefore be less than that outside, and this pressure difference provides a force on each sheet, pushing it towards the centre. The sheets therefore move together.

Another example of Bernoulli's Equation in action requires a little more by way of equipment, namely, a table-tennis ball and a thin tube. You will find that the table-tennis ball can be balanced on the vertical airstream created by blowing through the tube, as illustrated in Figure 4.3. The ball's situation is stable (for as long as you can keep blowing at a steady rate). If pushed a small distance sideways and then released, it will return to the centre of the stream.

A similar effect may be observed by placing a (not too ripe!) tomato, or other round object, in a kitchen sink beneath a steady stream of water from the tap.

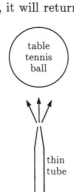

table tennis ball

thin tube

Figure 4.3   blow

Problem 4.1

Use Bernoulli's Equation to explain the stability of the table-tennis ball just described.

Having invited you to convince yourself that the qualitative predictions of Bernoulli's Equation are reasonable, we return to our two-dimensional flow model, and in particular to the flow past a disc of radius a, considered in Subsection 3.1. The velocity function in this case (with circulation $2\pi c$ around the disc) is

$$q_{a,c}(z) = \overline{1 - \frac{a^2}{z^2} - \frac{ic}{z}}.$$

Equation (3.4)

Problem 4.2

(a) Use Bernoulli's Equation to show that the pressure distribution of this flow past the disc is

$$p(z) = p_0 - \frac{\rho}{2}\left(1 - \frac{a^2}{z^2} - \frac{ic}{z}\right)\left(1 - \frac{a^2}{\bar{z}^2} + \frac{ic}{\bar{z}}\right).$$

(b) Find the pressure distribution on the boundary of the disc,

$$\left\{ae^{it} : 0 \le t < 2\pi\right\},$$

giving your answer in terms of p_0, ρ, c/a and $\sin t$.

(c) Deduce that the pressure distribution on the boundary is symmetric about the imaginary axis, and that if $c = 0$ it is also symmetric about the real axis. (As a result, the horizontal component of the total force on the obstacle due to the fluid is zero, and the vertical component is also zero if $c = 0$.)

From an expression for the pressure distribution on the boundary of an obstacle, as obtained in one particular case in Problem 4.2(b), it is possible to deduce the total force caused by pressure exerted on the obstacle due to the fluid flow. We show how to obtain this force in the next subsection.

4.2 Total force on the obstacle

The results in this subsection establish the total force on any obstacle caused by a flow which is a solution to the Obstacle Problem. This total force is caused by the effects of pressure around the boundary of the obstacle. Pressure is magnitude of force per unit area, but in our two-dimensional model one of the dimensions of area is directed into the page, perpendicular to the complex plane which we are using. Hence, the effect of the pressure distribution p, on a small segment of the (cross-sectional) boundary of length δs, is a force (per unit length into the page) of approximate magnitude $p(z)\delta s$, where z lies on the boundary segment concerned. This force is directed into the obstacle and perpendicular to the boundary at z, as illustrated in Figure 4.4.

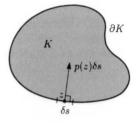

Figure 4.4

The total force on the obstacle K is the 'sum' of all such contributions around the boundary ∂K, where the sum has to take account of the directions as well as the magnitudes of the force contributions.

In order to calculate this force we now suppose that the boundary ∂K of the obstacle is a simple-closed smooth path of length L, which is traversed anticlockwise with unit-speed parametrization $\gamma : [0, L] \longrightarrow \partial K$ (so that $\gamma(L) = \gamma(0)$). Then, for each $s \in [0, L]$, the unit vector $\gamma'(s)$ is a tangent vector to the path and directed in the anticlockwise sense, as shown in Figure 4.5.

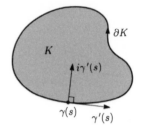

Figure 4.5

This figure also shows that the effect on $\gamma'(s)$ of multiplying by $i = e^{i\pi/2}$ is to rotate the vector by $\pi/2$ anticlockwise, producing another unit vector $i\gamma'(s)$, which is directed into K and perpendicular to the boundary ∂K at the point $z = \gamma(s)$. The corresponding force contribution (directed along $i\gamma'(s)$), for a length δs of the boundary which includes $\gamma(s)$, is approximately

$$p(\gamma(s))\delta s \times i\gamma'(s) = ip(\gamma(s))\gamma'(s)\delta s.$$

From these observations, it can be shown that the total force F acting on K (per unit length into the page) is

$$F = i \int_0^L p(\gamma(s))\gamma'(s)\, ds. \tag{4.2}$$

Special names are given to the real and imaginary parts of the force F.

Note that F is a (complex) constant. With an appropriate change to the limits of integration, the same formula is valid for any equivalent parametrization of ∂K.

Definitions If F is the total force acting on an obstacle, due to a fluid flow whose velocity function satisfies the Obstacle Problem, then

(a) $\operatorname{Re} F$ is called the **drag** on the obstacle;

(b) $\operatorname{Im} F$ is called the **lift** on the obstacle.

For the boundary of the disc of radius a, considered in Problem 4.2, we have the unit-speed parametrization

$$\gamma(s) = ae^{is/a} \qquad (s \in [0, 2\pi a]),$$

which is obtained from the standard parametrization $\gamma_1(t) = ae^{it}$ $(t \in [0, 2\pi])$ by putting $s = at$. Now

$$\gamma'(s) = ie^{is/a} = ie^{it},$$

and so, in this case, Equation (4.2) becomes

$$F = i \int_0^{2\pi} p\left(ae^{it}\right) ie^{it} a \, dt$$

$$= -a \int_0^{2\pi} p\left(ae^{it}\right) e^{it} dt.$$

Problem 4.3

By using the above formula for F, and the expression

$$p\left(ae^{it}\right) = p_0 - \frac{\rho}{2}\left(2\sin t - \frac{c}{a}\right)^2,$$

from the solution to Problem 4.2(b), find the total force (per unit length into the page) on a cylinder of radius a, due to a uniform flow with circulation $2\pi c$ around the obstacle. What are the lift and the drag in this case?

The result which you found in the particular case in Problem 4.3 (that is, zero drag and positive lift for negative circulation) generalizes to all obstacles. In order to show this we first re-express Equation (4.2) as follows.

Theorem 4.1 Blasius' Theorem

Let q be a solution to the Obstacle Problem for an obstacle K, whose boundary ∂K is a simple-closed smooth path, and suppose that q has a continuous extension to ∂K. Then the conjugate of the total force acting on the obstacle is

$$\overline{F} = \tfrac{1}{2}i\rho \int_{\partial K} (\overline{q}(z))^2 \, dz, \tag{4.3}$$

where ρ is the density of the fluid.

This result was published by H. Blasius in 1910. A similar theorem, which also bears his name, states that the *moment* (turning effect) M about 0, experienced by the obstacle due to the flow, is given by

$$M = -\tfrac{1}{2}\rho \operatorname{Re} \int_{\partial K} z(\overline{q}(z))^2 \, dz.$$

Remark If K is an obstacle whose boundary is not a simple-closed smooth path, then the integral in Equation (4.3) may not be defined. In this case we take the conjugate of the force acting on the obstacle to be

$$\overline{F} = \tfrac{1}{2}i\rho \int_{\Gamma} (\overline{q}(z))^2 dz, \tag{4.4}$$

where Γ is any simple-closed contour surrounding K. This is plausible for two reasons:

1. the integral in Equation (4.4) is independent of the choice of simple-closed contour Γ surrounding K because the function $z \longmapsto (\overline{q}(z))^2$ is analytic on $\mathbb{C} - K$, and so Cauchy's Theorem can be applied as in the proof of the Shrinking Contour Theorem (*Unit B2*, Theorem 1.4);

2. it can be shown that if ∂K *is* a simple-closed smooth path, then the integrals in Equations (4.3) and (4.4) are equal.

Proof On using Bernoulli's Equation to substitute for $p(\gamma(s))$ in Equation (4.2), we obtain

$$F = i \int_0^L \left(p_0 - \tfrac{1}{2}\rho|q(\gamma(s))|^2\right) \gamma'(s) \, ds.$$

This may be simplified by noting that

$$\int_0^L p_0 \gamma'(s) \, ds = p_0(\gamma(L) - \gamma(0)) = 0.$$

The complex conjugate of F is therefore

$$\overline{F} = \overline{\left(-\tfrac{1}{2}i\rho \int_0^L |q(\gamma(s))|^2 \gamma'(s)\,ds\right)}$$

$$= \tfrac{1}{2}i\rho \int_0^L |q(\gamma(s))|^2 \overline{\gamma'(s)}\,ds.$$

Now since γ is a unit-speed parametrization, we have $\gamma'(s) = e^{i\phi}$, for some ϕ, and hence $\overline{\gamma'(s)} = e^{-i\phi}$.

Also, ∂K is made up of streamlines of the flow, so that if $q_T(s)$ denotes the component of $q(\gamma(s))$ in the direction of $\gamma'(s)$, then

$$q(\gamma(s)) = q_T(s)e^{i\phi} \qquad \text{and} \qquad \overline{q}(\gamma(s)) = q_T(s)e^{-i\phi}.$$

Hence

$$|q(\gamma(s))|^2 = q(\gamma(s))\overline{q}(\gamma(s)) = (q_T(s))^2 = (\overline{q}(\gamma(s)))^2 e^{2i\phi},$$

and so the integrand is

$$|q(\gamma(s))|^2 \overline{\gamma'(s)} = (\overline{q}(\gamma(s)))^2 e^{2i\phi} e^{-i\phi} = (\overline{q}(\gamma(s)))^2 \gamma'(s).$$

Thus we obtain the required formula

$$\overline{F} = \tfrac{1}{2}i\rho \int_0^L (\overline{q}(\gamma(s)))^2 \gamma'(s)\,ds = \tfrac{1}{2}i\rho \int_{\partial K} (\overline{q}(z))^2 dz. \quad \blacksquare$$

Problem 4.4

Show that applying Blasius' Theorem to the conjugate velocity function

$$\overline{q_{a,c}}(z) = 1 - \frac{a^2}{z^2} - \frac{ic}{z}$$

gives a more rapid derivation of the result of Problem 4.3.

The next theorem is the promised generalization of the result of Problem 4.3.

Theorem 4.2 Kutta–Joukowski Lift Theorem

Let q be a solution to the Obstacle Problem for an obstacle K, with circulation $2\pi c$ around K. Then the obstacle experiences a total force

$$F = -2\pi c\rho i,$$

that is,

(a) a zero drag, and

(b) a lift of $-2\pi c\rho$.

Wilhelm Martin Kutta (1867–1944) spent most of his life in Munich, where he became a professor. He was a pioneer of two-dimensional wing theory, and discovered this result in 1902. It was found independently by Joukowski in 1906.

Proof Since the velocity function q is a solution of the Obstacle Problem, its conjugate $\overline{q}$ is analytic on $\mathbb{C} - K$ and $\lim_{z\to\infty} \overline{q}(z) = \lim_{z\to\infty} q(z) = 1$. Hence $\overline{q}$ has a removable singularity at ∞ and so, if K is contained in the disc $\{z : |z| \le R\}$, then $\overline{q}$ has a Laurent series of the form

$$\overline{q}(z) = 1 + \frac{a_{-1}}{z} + \frac{a_{-2}}{z^2} + \cdots, \qquad \text{for } |z| > R. \tag{4.5}$$

We can now express a_{-1} in terms of the circulation $2\pi c$ around K. From Equation (1.7), we have

$$\mathcal{C}_\Gamma + i\mathcal{F}_\Gamma = \int_\Gamma \overline{q}(z)\,dz,$$

where $\mathcal{C}_\Gamma$ and $\mathcal{F}_\Gamma$ are, respectively, the circulation along and flux across any simple-closed contour Γ which surrounds K.

This proof is for the case where ∂K is a simple-closed contour to which q has a continuous extension.

The function $g(w) = \overline{q}(1/w)$ has a removable singularity at 0, since

$$\lim_{w\to 0} g(w) = 1.$$

Taking Γ to lie outside the disc $\{z : |z| \le R\}$, we obtain

$$
\begin{aligned}
\mathcal{C}_\Gamma + i\mathcal{F}_\Gamma &= \int_\Gamma \left(1 + \frac{a_{-1}}{z} + \frac{a_{-2}}{z^2} + \cdots\right) dz \\
&= \int_\Gamma \frac{a_{-1}}{z}\,dz + \int_\Gamma \left(1 + \frac{a_{-2}}{z^2} + \cdots\right) dz \\
&= 2\pi i a_{-1}.
\end{aligned}
$$

The integral $\displaystyle\int_\Gamma \left(1 + \frac{a_{-2}}{z^2} + \cdots\right) dz$ is zero because the integrand has a primitive on $\{z : |z| > R\}$; see Step (e) of the proof of Laurent's Theorem in *Unit B4*, for similar reasoning.

Since $\mathcal{F}_\Gamma = 0$ (see Remark 4 following the Obstacle Problem) and $\mathcal{C}_\Gamma = 2\pi c$, we deduce that

$$
a_{-1} = -ic. \tag{4.6}
$$

Now, by the remark following Blasius' Theorem,

$$
\overline{F} = \tfrac{1}{2}i\rho \int_\Gamma (\overline{q}(z))^2 dz,
$$

where, as above, the simple-closed contour Γ lies outside the disc $\{z : |z| \le R\}$. Hence, using Equations (4.5) and (4.6), we have

$$
\begin{aligned}
\overline{F} &= \tfrac{1}{2}i\rho \int_\Gamma \left(1 - \frac{ic}{z} + \frac{a_{-2}}{z^2} + \cdots\right)^2 dz \\
&= \tfrac{1}{2}i\rho \int_\Gamma \left(1 - \frac{2ic}{z} + \left(2a_{-2} - c^2\right)\frac{1}{z^2} + \cdots\right) dz \\
&= \tfrac{1}{2}i\rho(-2ic)2\pi i = 2\pi c\rho i,
\end{aligned}
$$

so that $F = -2\pi c\rho i$, as required. ∎

With this result in mind, we return to the subject of aerofoils. In Problem 3.9(b), you saw that a symmetric Joukowski aerofoil with its axis on the real axis can have a finite limiting velocity $\lim_{z \to 2a} q(z)$ at its trailing edge if and only if there is no circulation. In Problem 3.10(c), this was generalized to the case of a symmetric aerofoil with angle of attack ϕ, showing that $\lim_{z \to 2\alpha} q(z)$ exists if and only if

$$
c = -2(a + b)\sin\phi,
$$

where $2\pi c$ is the circulation around the aerofoil.

In each case, if the circulation does not have the specific value indicated, then the flow velocity q is unbounded near the trailing edge. Such unbounded values in the model do not correspond with the real world, and this provides a motivation for avoiding such a situation. Moreover, Bernoulli's Equation predicts that negative pressure will be encountered in a region where q is unbounded. However, negative pressure is not an effect observed in nature.

The only way around this difficulty, within the scope of our current model, is to assume that the circulation takes precisely the value required to avoid the problem. This is the purpose of the following hypothesis.

Kutta–Joukowski Hypothesis

The circulation around a Joukowski aerofoil is such that the flow velocity q is bounded throughout the flow region, and $q(z)$ tends to a limit as z approaches the trailing edge of the aerofoil.

Remarks

1 This hypothesis, as well as being convenient in pinning down a specific value for the circulation, is in good agreement with experimental observations.

2 For a value of c which satisfies the Kutta–Joukowski Hypothesis, there is just one stagnation point on the boundary ∂K, whereas for nearby values of c there are two stagnation points. Roughly speaking, therefore, the effect described by the hypothesis is achieved by 'placing a stagnation point (zero) on top of a singularity'.

Problem 4.5

How does the lift on a symmetric Joukowski aerofoil depend on the angle of attack ϕ, assuming that the Kutta–Joukowski Hypothesis holds? Does this agree with what you know of aeroplane wings?

The solution to Problem 4.5 suggests that the model which we have constructed is only partially successful in describing fluid flows in the real world. In the next subsection, we consider just how good the model is.

4.3 Successes and limitations of the model

In this subsection, we assess the usefulness of studying model fluid flows. From the point of view of the current course, this unit has demonstrated the applicability of many of the complex analysis results and ideas introduced earlier. While this should have helped you to understand and appreciate these ideas further, it is not a reason to accept the model uncritically.

This subsection is intended for reading only.

On the plus side, the streamline pictures for the solution to the disc version of the Obstacle Problem, for various values of the circulation (see Figure 3.2), can be shown experimentally to have some validity, and a lift due to the circulation is observed. Also, for small values of the angle of attack presented by an aerofoil to the oncoming airstream, the prediction of lift being increased by raising the leading edge of the wing (Problem 4.5) is certainly borne out. In level flight, this upward lift force balances the downward pull due to gravity. Variation of the angle of attack allows an aircraft to climb (greater angle than for level flight) or descend (lesser angle) in a controlled fashion.

There is, however, a definite limit to the validity of this prediction, as pointed out in the solution to Problem 4.5. If the angle of attack becomes too large then stalling occurs; that is, the strength of the lift force decreases dramatically, and an aeroplane connected to the aerofoil would fall out of the sky.

There is also the question of the physical mechanism which produces the circulation necessary for lift to be provided. Our model contains circulation almost as an arbitrary ingredient whose value can be altered at will, except in the case of an aerofoil where the Kutta–Joukowski Hypothesis provides some rationale for picking a specific value for circulation. Even this rationale may seem dubious, since it arises from the desire to eliminate unbounded velocity values, though there is good experimental support for it.

The Kutta–Joukowski Lift Theorem is curious in two respects. Firstly, it predicts zero drag, that is, an absence of any force component in the direction of the incoming fluid stream. This prediction is seriously at odds with observation: for example, the table-tennis ball in a jet of air (see Problem 4.1 and the text before it) is maintained by the jet at some distance above the top of the tube through which air is blown, at the point where the drag due to the jet exactly balances the weight of (gravitational force on) the ball. In the absence of drag, the ball would descend to the mouth of the tube.

The mismatch here between the prediction of the model and experimental observation is known as *d'Alembert's Paradox.* Jean Le Rond d'Alembert (1717–83) was a leading French mathematician, a philosopher and a friend of Voltaire. His *Traité de l'Équilibre et du Mouvement des Fluides* was published in 1744, and the *Théorie Générale des Vents* in 1745.

Secondly, the Kutta–Joukowski Lift Theorem predicts, for any obstacle, a lift force which depends only on the circulation and fluid density, and is therefore independent of the object's shape or dimensions. This seems to suggest that the aerofoil shape is unnecessary, and that any obstacle, no matter what its profile, would be lifted equally by a given circulation. Again, this prediction is not what is observed in practice, although the circulation can depend to some extent on the shape of the body itself.

Clearly our model is lacking in some significant respect. Its major shortcomings arise because we have assumed the fluid flow to be *locally circulation-free*. In fact, non-zero circulation around small closed contours is *always* present in a moving fluid sufficiently close to a solid boundary. The mechanism which produces this local rotation is viscosity, or fluid friction. Viscosity is a feature of a fluid which can be measured, and may be thought of as describing the 'degree of stickiness' of the fluid.

Viscosity is caused by intermolecular forces acting within the fluid.

Clearly, some fluids are more viscous ('sticky') than others, as exemplified by the different behaviours of treacle and water at normal room temperatures. However, all real fluids have *some* viscosity, and an important consequence of this is that *all real fluids adhere to the boundary of any obstacle past which they flow*.

Thus an improved model, which takes viscosity into account, must impose a stronger condition on the behaviour of the flow velocity close to the boundary. Roughly speaking, what we now require is that the boundary should 'consist entirely of stagnation points'. There are indeed more advanced models of fluid flow which include the effects of viscosity. However, since the locally circulation-free condition must be dropped, these models cannot use complex analysis in the way that has been done here, as pointed out in the remark following Problem 2.1.

This requirement, which amounts to taking the limit of flow velocity to be zero as each boundary point is approached, is called the *no-slip condition* for viscous fluids.

All is not lost, however, as regards the application of our first model. Often the effects of fluid viscosity are significant only in a narrow region called the *boundary layer*, in the immediate vicinity of the obstacle. It is then reasonable to ignore the viscosity of the fluid except within the boundary layer, and to apply the original model to flow in the exterior region. Appropriate matching of models is needed at the interface between these two flow regimes. For example, the successful prediction for an aerofoil of increasing lift for increasing (but small) angle of attack corresponds to cases where the boundary layer around the aerofoil is narrow. (In fact, the aerofoil shape is of interest and practical use primarily because it achieves this narrow boundary layer.) At larger angles of attack, the boundary layer *separates* from the upper surface of the aerofoil (see Figure 4.6), leading to a large area in which the predictions of an inviscid (non-viscous) model are invalid.

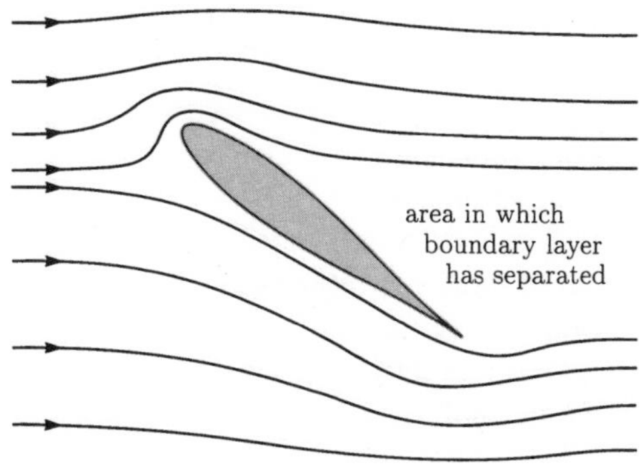

area in which boundary layer has separated

Figure 4.6

The circulation which is present for an aerofoil, and creates the lift on it, arises from the action of viscosity within the boundary layer. Similarly, the circulation considered in the context of a circular cylinder (with a disc as cross-section), in Subsection 3.1, may be thought of as created by the cylinder being *spun* in the clockwise direction (for negative c), with the 'obstacle boundary' now being at the outside of a narrow boundary layer.

The lift force predicted by our model in such a case is certainly observable, and its presence is known as the *Magnus Effect*. The direction of this force is always from the side of the obstacle where the circulation and uniform stream oppose each other, and towards that where they reinforce each other.

For example, if a football is kicked from right to left, say, with a spin which is clockwise when viewed from above (see Figure 4.7), then its trajectory will deviate to the right of its initial direction, producing the so-called 'banana kick'. The effects of top-spin or back-spin on tennis balls may be predicted in a similar manner.

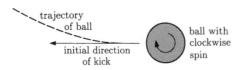

Figure 4.7

The Magnus Effect was at one time put to use in a form of ship propulsion, using tall vertical cylinders mounted on deck and known as *Flettner Rotors*. In the presence of a wind, rotation of the cylinders produced a horizontal 'lift' force, at right angles to the direction of the wind. Rotating cylinders have also been attached to ship rudders, providing dramatic improvements in manoeuvrability at low speeds.

We have looked so far at the shortcomings associated with our modelling assumption that the flow is locally circulation-free. We also assumed that the flow is *locally flux-free*, and pointed out in Subsection 1.2 that, for a fluid of constant density, this condition is equivalent to the Principle of Conservation of Mass.

A fluid of constant density is said to be *incompressible*. In reality, no fluid is completely incompressible (it is compressibility which permits sound waves to travel through a fluid), but liquids are much less compressible than gases. Since fluids are compressible to some degree, they are not locally flux-free in a precise sense.

Where aerofoils are concerned, the predictions of models based on the assumption of incompressible (locally flux-free) flow are reasonable for airstream velocities below 100 m s^{-1}, which is much less than the speed of sound (about 330 m s^{-1}). At higher velocities, the theory of compressible flows is required. The compressibility of air has the effect of increasing slightly the lift for a given angle of attack, and of raising the extent to which the aerofoil can be tilted before stalling occurs.

Mathematical modelling is an iterative process. It is in the nature of modelling that a first model will be only partially effective in its task, and that subsequent improvements will probably be required. This implies no devaluation of the first model, since it is necessary to make sufficient simplifications when starting to consider a situation to ensure that some progress is made. Within its limitations, the model of fluid flows introduced in this unit may be judged relatively successful, since it predicts significant physical phenomena which are observable in practice and allows us to see the direction in which a further model must improve on the original.

Heinrich Gustav Magnus (1802–70) was a German chemist and physicist, and a Professor at Berlin University. He explained the Magnus Effect in 1852, after interest in the subject had been aroused by deviations to the paths of bullets in a cross-wind.

A football does not have constant two-dimensional cross-section, but the same effect is observed for spinning objects which do. As far as the ball is concerned, the oncoming airstream moves initially from left to right. The 'lift' for the football here is actually in the horizontal direction. Top-spin produces a downward 'lift' force and back-spin an upward one.

Anton Flettner was a German naval engineer, and built a ship with these rotors in 1924. Experiments with the ship were satisfactory, but ships propelled by ordinary engines proved to be economically superior.

4.4 Derivation of Bernoulli's Equation

We assume, as earlier in the unit, that the flow is two-dimensional and steady, and that the fluid has constant density. As you may recall, Newton's Second Law in single-particle mechanics states that

This subsection is intended for reading only.

force = mass × acceleration.

Here we require a version of this law which is applicable at each point of the fluid. This can be obtained by considering both the force acting on and the mass of a small volume of fluid, and then letting the volume size tend to zero. This gives, at each point,

force per unit volume = density × acceleration,

or in symbols,

$$F(z) = \rho \frac{d^2 z}{dt^2}, \qquad (4.7)$$

where $F(z)$ is the force per unit volume at z and ρ is the constant fluid density.

Note that $F(z)$ is the force acting at the point z on the *fluid* rather than on an obstacle.

The velocity of the fluid is given by $dz/dt = q(z)$, so that its acceleration may be expressed as

$$\frac{d^2 z}{dt^2} = \frac{dq(z)}{dt}. \qquad (4.8)$$

Using Equation (4.8) to substitute for d^2z/dt^2 in Equation (4.7), and then taking the complex conjugate, we have

$$\overline{F}(z) = \rho \frac{d\overline{q}(z)}{dt}.$$

Since $\overline{q}$ is an analytic function, this can be expressed as

$$\overline{F}(z) = \rho \overline{q}\,'(z)\frac{dz}{dt},$$

or simply as

$$\overline{F}(z) = \rho q(z)\overline{q}\,'(z). \qquad (4.9)$$

This expression for the conjugate force per unit volume acting on the fluid will be of use shortly.

We now relate the force per unit volume acting within the fluid to the pressure of the fluid. We shall ignore the effects of any other contributions to the force per unit volume, such as those due to gravity or to viscosity within the fluid.

Suppose that $\gamma(s)$ is a unit-speed parametrization of any line segment within the flow region of the complex plane, and consider a small cylinder, of cross-sectional area A, whose axis lies along the line segment. The ends of the cylinder are at $\gamma(s)$ and $\gamma(s+h)$, as shown in Figure 4.8, so that the length of the cylinder is h.

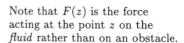

Figure 4.8

The force per unit volume $F(\gamma(s))$ leads to an approximate force $F(\gamma(s))Ah$ on the cylinder of fluid, where the relative error of the approximation decreases as A and h tend to zero. We shall restrict attention to the component of this force in the direction of $\gamma'(s)$, which is $F_T(s)Ah$.

The fluid pressure causes a 'force distribution' acting at each point of the cylinder in a direction perpendicular to the cylinder's surface. However, the directions of the forces acting on the curved part of the surface are perpendicular to the direction $\gamma'(s)$, and hence do not contribute to the force component in this direction. The remaining forces due to the pressure are approximately $p(\gamma(s))A$, in the direction of $\gamma'(s)$, and $p(\gamma(s+h))A$, in the opposite direction, as shown in Figure 4.9.

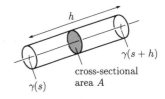
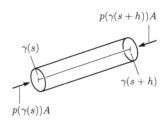

Figure 4.9

It follows that

$$F_T(s)Ah \cong p(\gamma(s))A - p(\gamma(s+h))A;$$

that is

$$F_T(s) \cong \frac{p(\gamma(s)) - p(\gamma(s+h))}{h}.$$

The relative error implicit in use of the $\cong$ sign tends to zero as h tends to zero, and so in this limit we obtain

$$F_T(s) = -\frac{dp(\gamma(s))}{ds}. \qquad (4.10)$$

Now $\gamma'(s)$ has modulus 1 so, by the first of Equations (1.2), the component $F_T(s)$ of $F(\gamma(s))$ in the direction of $\gamma'(s)$ may be written as

$$F_T(s) = \mathrm{Re}(\overline{F}(\gamma(s))\gamma'(s)). \qquad (4.11)$$

Equations (1.2) were expressed in terms of the fluid velocity function q, but they apply also to any other function.

On applying Equations (4.11) and (4.9) to Equation (4.10), we find that

$$\mathrm{Re}(\rho q(\gamma(s))\overline{q}'(\gamma(s))\gamma'(s)) = -\frac{dp(\gamma(s))}{ds};$$

that is,

$$\rho\,\mathrm{Re}\left(q(\gamma(s))\frac{d\overline{q}(\gamma(s))}{ds}\right) = -\frac{dp(\gamma(s))}{ds}.$$

This can be rewritten as

$$-\frac{dp(\gamma(s))}{ds} = \frac{\rho}{2}\left(q(\gamma(s))\frac{d\overline{q}(\gamma(s))}{ds} + \overline{q}(\gamma(s))\frac{dq(\gamma(s))}{ds}\right)$$

$$= \tfrac{1}{2}\rho\frac{d}{ds}(q(\gamma(s))\overline{q}(\gamma(s))).$$

Note that
$$\mathrm{Re}(z_1 z_2) = \tfrac{1}{2}(z_1 z_2 + \overline{z_1}\,\overline{z_2}).$$

By writing $q(z)\overline{q}(z) = |q(z)|^2$, and integrating with respect to s, we obtain Bernoulli's Equation,

$$p(\gamma(s)) + \tfrac{1}{2}\rho|q(\gamma(s))|^2 = p_0,$$

where p_0 is a constant. Since our derivation referred to an arbitrary line segment in the fluid, Bernoulli's Equation holds throughout the fluid; that is,

$$p(z) + \tfrac{1}{2}\rho|q(z)|^2 = p_0.$$

EXERCISES

Section 1

Exercise 1.1 Find the component of $q(z) = 3e^{7i\pi/12}$ (at any point z) in the direction specified by each of the following complex numbers.

(a) $e^{-2i\pi/3}$ (b) $-ie^{-2i\pi/3}$

Exercise 1.2 Use Equations (1.2) to show that, if θ is any angle, then a flow velocity $q(z)$ can be expressed in terms of its components by

$$q(z) = (q_\theta(z) - iq_{(\theta-\pi/2)}(z))e^{i\theta}.$$

Exercise 1.3 Consider the flow velocity function

$$q(z) = 1 - \frac{1}{\bar{z}^2} \qquad (z \in \mathbb{C} - \{0\}).$$

(a) Let Γ be the unit circle $\{z : |z| = 1\}$. Use Equation (1.7) to show that q has zero circulation along Γ, and zero flux across Γ.

(b) Show that q is a model flow velocity function, using in turn:
  (i) Theorem 1.2;   (ii) Theorem 1.3.

Section 2

Exercise 2.1

(a) Draw a rough sketch of the streamlines for a uniform flow with complex potential $2z$, on which is superposed a source of strength 4π at the origin. Find the position of the single stagnation point of the flow.

(b) The curved streamlines which approach the stagnation point may be taken as the boundary of a blunt object placed in the uniform flow. Find equations to describe this boundary, and calculate the 'maximum width' of the object perpendicular to the flow.

Exercise 2.2 Prove that, if a model flow velocity function with domain $\mathbb{C}$ is bounded, then the flow is uniform.

(*Hint*: Use Liouville's Theorem.)   *Unit B2, Theorem 2.2*

Section 3

Exercise 3.1 By considering the stream function of the flow with complex potential

$$\Omega(z) = z + \frac{a^2}{z} \qquad (z \in \mathbb{C} - K_a),$$

where $K_a = \{z : |z| \le a\}$, find the equation of the streamline which passes through the point $2ai$. Hence find the limiting value of the distance between this streamline and the real axis, far from the disc K_a.

Exercise 3.2 Let K_a denote the closed disc $\{z : |z| \le a\}$. Consider the obstacle (see the figure in the margin)

$$K = [-2, -1] \cup K_1 \cup [1, 2].$$

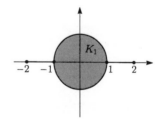

(a) Show that the Joukowski function J is a one-one conformal mapping from $\mathbb{C} - K$ onto $\mathbb{C} - \left[-\frac{5}{2}, \frac{5}{2}\right]$.

(b) Find a value of a for which the function

$$J_a(w) = w + \frac{a^2}{w}$$

is a one-one conformal mapping of $\mathbb{C} - K_a$ onto $\mathbb{C} - \left[-\frac{5}{2}, \frac{5}{2}\right]$.

(c) Show that the Obstacle Problem for K, with circulation $2\pi c$ around K, has solution

$$q(z) = \overline{\left(1 - \frac{ic}{J(z)\sqrt{1 - 25/(2J(z))^2}}\right)} J'(z).$$

(*Hint*: You may assume that the function $f = J_a^{-1} \circ J$ satisfies Condition (3.5). Also, find the velocity function from the complex potential function, using the fact that $\Omega_{a,c} = J_a - ic\,\mathrm{Log}$ and the approach of Problem 3.5.)

Exercise 3.3 Suppose that $0 < a < r$. Let K be the obstacle whose boundary is the ellipse

$$\partial K = \left\{ x + iy : \frac{x^2}{(r - a^2/r)^2} + \frac{y^2}{(r + a^2/r)^2} = 1 \right\},$$

whose major axis lies along the imaginary axis (see the figure in the margin).

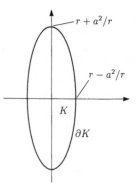

Show that the Obstacle Problem for K, with circulation $2\pi c$ around K, has solution

$$q(z) = 1 - \overline{\left(\frac{r^2 + a^2 + icJ_{ai}^{-1}(z)}{\left(J_{ai}^{-1}(z) \right)^2 + a^2} \right)}.$$

(*Hint*: Find the flow velocity function from the complex potential function.)

Section 4

Exercise 4.1 In Problem 3.7, you found that the model flow past the 'plate' $K = [-2a, 2a]$, with circulation $2\pi c$ around K, has a flow velocity

$$q(z) = 1 - \overline{\left(\frac{ic}{z\sqrt{1 - 4a^2/z^2}} \right)}.$$

Find the force on the plate by applying Equation (4.4), the modified form of Blasius' Theorem.

(*Hint*: The circulation around K is given by

$$2\pi c = \int_\Gamma \bar{q}(z)\, dz,$$

where Γ is any simple-closed contour surrounding K.)

Exercise 4.2 The asymmetric Joukowski aerofoil K, shown on the left of the figure below, has boundary $\partial K = J(\partial D)$, where

$$D = \{w : |w - \beta| \le |1 - \beta|\} \qquad \text{and} \qquad \operatorname{Re} \beta < 0.$$

It can be shown that the Joukowski function J is a one-one mapping of $\mathbb{C} - D$ onto $\mathbb{C} - K$.

The condition $\operatorname{Re} \beta < 0$ ensures that the critical point $w = -1$ lies within D, with its image $z = -2$ within K. For $\operatorname{Re} \beta = 0$ (but $\operatorname{Im} \beta > 0$), the circle ∂D would pass through both of the critical points $w = \pm 1$. In this case, the image $J(\partial D)$ is a circular arc in the upper z-plane, from $z = -2$ to $z = 2$, and J is a one-one mapping of $\mathbb{C} - D$ onto $\mathbb{C} - J(\partial D)$. The case for $\operatorname{Re} \beta = 0$ is indicated by the broken curves on the diagram.

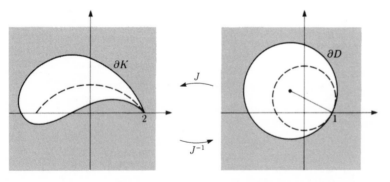

Show that, if the Kutta–Joukowski Hypothesis holds, then the force acting on K due to the flow is

$$F = 4\pi\rho i \operatorname{Im} \beta.$$

SOLUTIONS TO THE PROBLEMS

Section 1

1.1 (a) For $q(z) = z$, all of the arrows for $z \neq 0$ have direction Arg z, and so point radially outwards. At the origin, $z = 0$, there is a stagnation point.

(b) By using results from *Unit A1*, Subsection 2.3, we have that the direction of $q(z) = i/\overline{z}$ ($z \neq 0$) is given by

$$\text{Arg}(i/\overline{z}) = \text{Arg}\, i - \text{Arg}\, \overline{z} + 2n\pi$$
$$= \text{Arg}\, i + \text{Arg}\, z + 2n\pi$$
$$= \text{Arg}\, z + \pi/2 + 2n\pi,$$

where $n \in \mathbb{Z}$. The pattern is therefore as shown below. This is an example of a *vortex flow*.

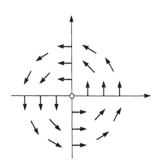

1.2 In each case, the streamline picture can be deduced from the corresponding arrow pattern in the solution to Problem 1.1, as shown in the following figures.

(a)

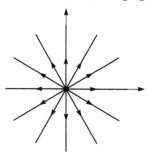

(b)

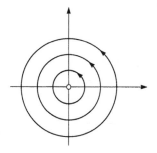

1.3 With $q(z) = 5e^{-i\pi/6}$ and $\theta = 2\pi/3$, we have, from Equation (1.1),

$$q_{2\pi/3}(z) = \text{Re}\left(\overline{5e^{-i\pi/6}}e^{2i\pi/3}\right)$$
$$= \text{Re}\left(5e^{i\pi/6}e^{2i\pi/3}\right)$$
$$= \text{Re}\left(5e^{5i\pi/6}\right)$$
$$= 5\cos\frac{5\pi}{6}$$
$$= -\tfrac{5}{2}\sqrt{3}.$$

1.4 From Equation (1.1), we have

$$q_\theta(z) = \text{Re}\left(\overline{q(z)}e^{i\theta}\right).$$

With $\theta - \pi/2$ in place of θ, this becomes

$$q_{(\theta - \pi/2)}(z) = \text{Re}\left(\overline{q(z)}e^{i(\theta - \pi/2)}\right)$$
$$= \text{Re}\left(\overline{q(z)}e^{i\theta}e^{-i\pi/2}\right)$$
$$= \text{Re}\left(-i\,\overline{q(z)}e^{i\theta}\right).$$

Now if $w = u + iv$ is any complex number, then

$$\text{Re}(-iw) = \text{Re}(v - iu) = v = \text{Im}\, w.$$

It follows that

$$q_{(\theta - \pi/2)}(z) = \text{Im}\left(\overline{q(z)}e^{i\theta}\right).$$

1.5 (a) If $\overline{q}(z) = z$ is the conjugate velocity function, then the velocity function itself is $q(z) = \overline{z}$. To draw the arrow pattern for this velocity function, note that $\overline{z}$ has the same real part as z, but an imaginary part of opposite sign. This gives a sketch like that below, using arrows of fixed length (except at 0, which is a stagnation point of the flow).

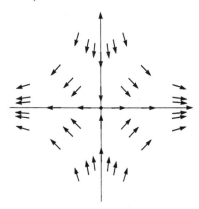

(b) If $\overline{q}(z) = 1/z$, then we have

$$q(z) = 1/\overline{z} \quad (z \in \mathbb{C} - \{0\}).$$

Now

$$\text{Arg}(q(z)) = \text{Arg}(1/\overline{z}) = \text{Arg}\, z,$$

so the direction of $q(z)$ is radially outwards. This leads to the same fixed length arrow pattern as in the solution to Problem 1.1(a), except that the origin should in this case be omitted.

(c) If $\overline{q}(z) = i/z$, then we have

$$q(z) = -i/\overline{z} \quad (z \in \mathbb{C} - \{0\}).$$

The picture is like that of the solution to Problem 1.1(b), but with all the arrows reversed.

1.6 **(a)** The velocity function $q(z) = z$ $(z \in \mathbb{C})$ has conjugate function $\bar{q}(z) = \bar{z}$. This is not an analytic function (see Problem 1.8 of *Unit A4*), so, by Theorem 1.2, q is not a model flow velocity function.

(b) For $q(z) = i/\bar{z}$ $(z \in \mathbb{C} - \{0\})$, the conjugate velocity function is $\bar{q}(z) = -i/z$. This function is analytic on $\mathbb{C} - \{0\}$ (see Problem 1.2 of *Unit A4*, and apply the Multiple Rule in Theorem 1.3 of that unit), so, by Theorem 1.2, q is a model flow velocity function.

1.7 **(a)** The flux of $q(z) = 1/\bar{z}$ across the unit circle Γ is (from Equation (1.7))

$$\mathcal{F}_\Gamma = \text{Im} \int_\Gamma \bar{q}(z)\, dz$$

$$= \text{Im} \int_\Gamma \frac{1}{z}\, dz$$

$$= \text{Im}(2\pi i) \quad \text{(by Cauchy's Integral Formula)}$$

$$= 2\pi.$$

(b) Similarly, the circulation along Γ of $q(z) = -i/\bar{z}$ is

$$\mathcal{C}_\Gamma = \text{Re} \int_\Gamma \bar{q}(z)\, dz$$

$$= \text{Re} \int_\Gamma \frac{i}{z}\, dz$$

$$= \text{Re}(-2\pi)$$

$$= -2\pi.$$

(c) In each of parts (a) and (b), the origin is excluded from the domain $\mathcal{R}$ of q, so that the inside of Γ (the unit circle) does *not* lie in $\mathcal{R}$. The function q is, therefore, still *locally* flux-free and circulation-free, in each case.

1.8 **(a)** By the Cauchy-Riemann Theorems (*Unit A4*, Subsection 2.1), if the partial derivatives of the real functions u, v with respect to x, y exist and are continuous on $\mathcal{R}$, then $u + iv$ is an analytic function on $\mathcal{R}$ if and only if

$$\frac{\partial u}{\partial x} = \frac{\partial v}{\partial y} \quad \text{and} \quad \frac{\partial v}{\partial x} = -\frac{\partial u}{\partial y} \quad \text{on } \mathcal{R}.$$

Now the velocity function $q = q_1 + iq_2$ has conjugate function $\bar{q} = q_1 - iq_2$, and q is a model flow velocity function on $\mathcal{R}$ if and only if $\bar{q}$ is analytic on $\mathcal{R}$ (by Theorem 1.2). Putting these results together, with $u = q_1$ and $v = -q_2$, we have that q is a model flow velocity function on $\mathcal{R}$ if and only if

$$\frac{\partial q_1}{\partial x} + \frac{\partial q_2}{\partial y} = 0 \quad \text{and} \quad \frac{\partial q_2}{\partial x} - \frac{\partial q_1}{\partial y} = 0 \quad \text{on } \mathcal{R}.$$

(b) The real and imaginary parts of

$$q(z) = \frac{i}{\bar{z}} = \frac{iz}{|z|^2} = \frac{i(x + iy)}{x^2 + y^2},$$

are, respectively,

$$q_1(x, y) = -\frac{y}{x^2 + y^2}, \quad q_2(x, y) = \frac{x}{x^2 + y^2}.$$

The partial derivatives of q_1 and q_2 are

$$\frac{\partial q_1}{\partial x} = \frac{2xy}{(x^2 + y^2)^2}, \quad \frac{\partial q_1}{\partial y} = \frac{y^2 - x^2}{(x^2 + y^2)^2},$$

$$\frac{\partial q_2}{\partial x} = \frac{y^2 - x^2}{(x^2 + y^2)^2}, \quad \frac{\partial q_2}{\partial y} = -\frac{2xy}{(x^2 + y^2)^2}.$$

Hence we find, if $z \neq 0$, that

$$\frac{\partial q_1}{\partial x} + \frac{\partial q_2}{\partial y} = 0 \quad \text{and} \quad \frac{\partial q_2}{\partial x} - \frac{\partial q_1}{\partial y} = 0.$$

By the result of part (a), $q(z) = i/\bar{z}$ $(z \in \mathbb{C} - \{0\})$ is therefore a model flow velocity function.

1.9 **(a)** For the velocity function $q(z) = z$, we have $q_1(x, y) = x$ and $q_2(x, y) = y$, so that

$$\frac{\partial q_2}{\partial x} - \frac{\partial q_1}{\partial y} = 0.$$

Hence, by Theorem 1.3, q is locally circulation-free. However, since

$$\frac{\partial q_1}{\partial x} + \frac{\partial q_2}{\partial y} = 1 + 1 = 2 \neq 0,$$

the function q is not locally flux-free.

(b) For the velocity function $q(z) = iz$, we have $q_1(x, y) = -y$ and $q_2(x, y) = x$, so that

$$\frac{\partial q_1}{\partial x} + \frac{\partial q_2}{\partial y} = 0,$$

showing q to be locally flux-free, by Theorem 1.3. However, since

$$\frac{\partial q_2}{\partial x} - \frac{\partial q_1}{\partial y} = 1 - (-1) = 2 \neq 0,$$

the function q is not locally circulation-free.

Section 2

2.1 The complex potential Ω is defined by

$$\Omega'(z) = \bar{q}(z).$$

With $\Omega(z) = \Phi(x, y) + i\Psi(x, y)$, we have

$$\Omega'(z) = \frac{\partial \Phi}{\partial x} + i\frac{\partial \Psi}{\partial x}$$

(by the Cauchy–Riemann Converse Theorem)

$$= \frac{\partial \Psi}{\partial y} + i\frac{\partial \Psi}{\partial x}$$

(by the Cauchy–Riemann Theorem).

On taking complex conjugates, we obtain

$$q(z) = \frac{\partial \Psi}{\partial y} - i\frac{\partial \Psi}{\partial x}.$$

2.2 A complex potential Ω is given by $\Omega'(z) = \bar{q}(z)$. Here we have

$$q(z) = \frac{-1 + 8i}{\bar{z}} \quad (z \in \mathbb{C} - \{0\}),$$

so we require for Ω a primitive of

$$\bar{q}(z) = -\frac{1 + 8i}{z}.$$

We need to choose a simply-connected subregion of $\mathbb{C} - \{0\}$ to be the domain of Ω, as discussed on the audio tape (see Frame 3). If the domain is chosen to be the cut plane $\mathbb{C}_\pi$, we may take

$$\Omega(z) = -(1 + 8i)\,\text{Log}\,z$$

$$= -(1 + 8i)(\log_e |z| + i\,\text{Arg}\,z).$$

The stream function is then

$$\text{Im}(\Omega(z)) = -(8 \log_e |z| + \text{Arg}\,z).$$

The equation for streamlines is $\text{Im}(\Omega(z)) = k$, where k is a constant; that is,

$$-8 \log_e |z| = k + \text{Arg}\,z.$$

Further manipulation of this equation gives

$$|z| = e^{-k/8} e^{-(\text{Arg}\,z)/8} = Ke^{-(\text{Arg}\,z)/8},$$

where $K = e^{-k/8}$ is another constant. As $\text{Arg}\,z$ increases from $-\pi$ to π, $|z|$ decreases exponentially. On joining this picture up across the negative real axis (using a logarithm function defined on a different cut plane), we see that the streamlines are spirals directed inwards, as shown below. This is a *whirlpool* or *spiral vortex* flow (combination of a sink and a vortex).

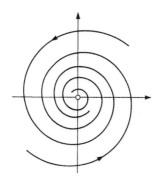

The source strength and vortex strength are, respectively, the flux across and circulation along any simple-closed contour Γ which surrounds the origin. These are, in turn, the respective imaginary and real parts of

$$\int_\Gamma \overline{q}(z)\,dz = \int_\Gamma -\frac{1+8i}{z}\,dz,$$

which, by Cauchy's Integral Formula, has the value

$$-2\pi i(1+8i) = 16\pi - 2\pi i.$$

Hence the flow has source strength -2π and vortex strength 16π.

2.3 **(a)** We have to show that

$$\overline{\Omega'(z)} = q(z), \quad \text{for } z \in \mathcal{R},$$

where $\mathcal{R} = \mathbb{C} - \{x \in \mathbb{R} : x \le h\}$. On $\mathcal{R}$,

$$\Omega'(z) = \text{Log}'(z) - \text{Log}'(z - h)$$
$$= \frac{1}{z} - \frac{1}{z-h},$$

so that

$$\overline{\Omega'(z)} = \frac{1}{\overline{z}} - \frac{1}{\overline{z} - h} = q(z),$$

as required.

(b) The complex potential

$$\Omega(z) = \text{Log}\,z - \text{Log}(z - h)$$

leads to the stream function

$$\text{Im}(\Omega(z)) = \text{Arg}\,z - \text{Arg}(z - h),$$

which must be constant along each streamline. Suppose first that z is in the upper half-plane.

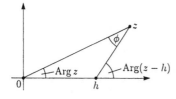

The angle ϕ marked on the diagram above is equal to $\text{Arg}(z - h) - \text{Arg}\,z$, since the exterior angle of any triangle is equal to the sum of its two interior opposite angles. Hence as z moves along a streamline, the angle ϕ remains constant. It follows that z moves along a circular arc passing through 0 and h. By symmetry, the centre of the circle lies on the line $x = \frac{1}{2}h$.

A similar conclusion is reached by considering z to be below the real axis. The real axis itself contains three streamlines, namely $]-\infty, 0[$, $]0, h[$ and $]h, \infty[$. The directions on the streamlines follow from the facts that $z = 0$ is a source and $z = h$ is a sink. The streamline diagram is therefore as follows.

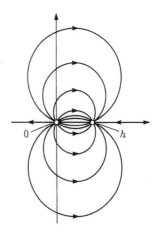

2.4 Taking the limit, we have

$$\lim_{h \to 0} q_h(z) = \lim_{h \to 0} \frac{1}{h}\left(\frac{1}{\overline{z}} - \frac{1}{\overline{z} - h}\right)$$
$$= \lim_{h \to 0} \frac{-h}{h\overline{z}(\overline{z} - h)}$$
$$= -\frac{1}{\overline{z}^2},$$

which is the velocity function for the doublet. The streamlines for the doublet are shown in Frame 6 of the audio tape.

Section 3

3.1 **(a)** The condition for stagnation points is $q(z) = 0$, or equivalently, $\overline{q}(z) = 0$. Here we have

$$\overline{q}(z) = 1 - \frac{a^2}{z^2}, \quad \text{for } z \in \mathbb{C} - \{0\},$$

so that the stagnation points satisfy

$$z^2 - a^2 = (z + a)(z - a) = 0.$$

Hence the only stagnation points are $z = \pm a$.

(b) Substitution of $z = ae^{it}$ into $q(z) = 1 - a^2/\overline{z}^2$ gives

$$q(ae^{it}) = 1 - \frac{a^2}{a^2 e^{-2it}}$$
$$= 1 - e^{2it}$$
$$= (e^{-it} - e^{it})e^{it}$$
$$= (-2i\sin t)e^{it}, \quad \text{for } 0 \le t \le 2\pi.$$

This gives the velocity of the flow at $z = ae^{it}$, on the circle $\{z : |z| = a\}$. The flow speed here is

$$\left|q(ae^{it})\right| = 2|\sin t|.$$

3.2 The quadratic equation
$$z^2 - icz - a^2 = 0$$
has solutions
$$z = \tfrac{1}{2}\left(ic \pm \sqrt{4a^2 - c^2}\right),$$
which are the stagnation points of the flow.

(a) For $-2a < c < 0$, we have $4a^2 - c^2 > 0$, so that the stagnation points have real parts $\pm\tfrac{1}{2}\sqrt{4a^2 - c^2}$ and imaginary part $\tfrac{1}{2}c$. The modulus in each case is
$$|z| = \tfrac{1}{2}\sqrt{(4a^2 - c^2) + c^2} = a,$$
so that both stagnation points lie on the circle $\{z : |z| = a\}$. They are below the real axis (since $c < 0$), and symmetrically placed on either side of the imaginary axis.

(b) For $c = -2a$, we have $4a^2 - c^2 = 0$, and so $z = \tfrac{1}{2}ic = -ia$. Thus there is a single stagnation point, which lies at the intersection of the circle $\{z : |z| = a\}$ and the imaginary axis.

(c) For $c < -2a$, we have $4a^2 - c^2 < 0$, so that the stagnation points are at
$$z = \tfrac{1}{2}i(c \pm \sqrt{c^2 - 4a^2}) = z_\pm, \text{ say.}$$
Both of these stagnation points are on the imaginary axis, and below the real axis (since $c < 0$ and $|c| > \sqrt{c^2 - 4a^2}$). Now since $c < -2a$, we have
$$\operatorname{Im} z_- = \tfrac{1}{2}(c - \sqrt{c^2 - 4a^2}) < \tfrac{1}{2}c < -a,$$
so that $|z_-| > a$, and z_- lies outside the circle $\{z : |z| = a\}$. Also $z_+ z_- = -a^2$, so that $|z_+| = a^2/|z_-| < a$, and z_+ lies inside the circle $\{z : |z| = a\}$.

3.3 We show that $q(z) = 1$ satisfies the three properties given in the statement of the Obstacle Problem.

Property (a)   Since $q(z) = 1$, $\lim_{z \to \infty} q(z) = 1$.

Property (b)   A complex potential function for q is
$$\Omega(z) = z \quad (z \in \mathbb{C} - K).$$
Let $\alpha \in \partial K = K$. Then
$$\lim_{z \to \alpha} \operatorname{Im}(\Omega(z)) = k,$$
where $k = \operatorname{Im}\alpha$, since $\operatorname{Im}\Omega$ has continuous extension to the whole of $\mathbb{C}$.

Note that $\operatorname{Im}\alpha$ is constant on ∂K because ∂K is a line segment parallel to the real axis.

Property (c)   Since $\bar{q}$ has analytic extension to the whole of $\mathbb{C}$, we have $\mathcal{C}_\Gamma = 0$, for any simple-closed contour Γ surrounding K.

3.4 The translation $f(z) = z - \beta$ is a one-one conformal mapping from $\mathbb{C} - K$ onto $\mathbb{C} - K_a$. Also f satisfies Condition (3.5), with $a_0 = -\beta$ and $a_{-1} = a_{-2} = \ldots = 0$. Thus, by the Flow Mapping Theorem, the velocity function which solves the Obstacle Problem for K, with circulation $2\pi c$ around K, is
$$q(z) = q_{a,c}(f(z))\overline{f'(z)}$$
$$= 1 - \overline{\frac{a^2}{(z - \beta)^2} - \frac{ic}{z - \beta}}, \quad \text{since } \overline{f'(z)} = 1.$$

3.5 By the Flow Mapping Theorem, the required complex potential function is
$$\Omega(z) = \Omega_{a,c}(f(z)),$$
where $f(z) = J^{-1}(z) = \tfrac{1}{2}(z + z\sqrt{1 - 4/z^2})$ and $a = 1$.
Using the hint, we have
$$\Omega(z) = \Omega_{1,c}\left(J^{-1}(z)\right)$$
$$= J\left(J^{-1}(z)\right) - ic\operatorname{Log}\left(J^{-1}(z)\right)$$
$$= z - ic\operatorname{Log}\left(\tfrac{1}{2}(z + z\sqrt{1 - 4/z^2})\right),$$
as required.

The velocity function is $q(z) = \overline{\Omega'(z)}$, where
$$\Omega'(z) = 1 - \frac{ic\left(J^{-1}\right)'(z)}{J^{-1}(z)}$$
$$= 1 - \frac{ic\left(1 - 1/\left(J^{-1}(z)\right)^2\right)^{-1}}{J^{-1}(z)} \quad \text{(as in Example 3.1)}$$
$$= 1 - \frac{ic}{J^{-1}(z) - 1/J^{-1}(z)}.$$
Hence, as in Example 3.1,
$$q(z) = 1 - \overline{\left(\frac{ic}{z\sqrt{1 - 4/z^2}}\right)}.$$

3.6 **(a)** The scaling $z_1 = z/a$ maps $\mathbb{C} - K_a$ onto $\mathbb{C} - K_1$; the Joukowski function $z_2 = J(z_1) = z_1 + 1/z_1$ maps $\mathbb{C} - K_1$ onto $\mathbb{C} - [-2, 2]$; the scaling $w = az_2$ maps $\mathbb{C} - [-2, 2]$ onto $\mathbb{C} - [-2a, 2a]$.

Since each of the above mappings is one-one, onto and conformal, the function
$$J_a(z) = z + \frac{a^2}{z} = a\left(z/a + \frac{1}{z/a}\right)$$
is a one-one conformal mapping from $\mathbb{C} - K_a$ onto $\mathbb{C} - [-2a, 2a]$.

The set ∂K_a is $\{ae^{it} : 0 \le t \le 2\pi\}$. The image under J_a of a typical point in this set is
$$J_a\left(ae^{it}\right) = ae^{it} + a^2/\left(ae^{it}\right)$$
$$= a\left(e^{it} + e^{-it}\right) = 2a\cos t.$$
Hence
$$J_a(\partial K_a) = \{2a\cos t : 0 \le t \le 2\pi\}$$
$$= [-2a, 2a],$$
as required.

(b) The inverse function $z = J_a^{-1}(w)$ is the composition of
the scaling $z_2 = w/a$;

the inverse Joukowski function
$$z_1 = J^{-1}(z_2) = \tfrac{1}{2}(z_2 + z_2\sqrt{1 - 4/z_2^2});$$
the scaling $z = az_1$.

Hence the required inverse function is
$$J_a^{-1}(w) = \tfrac{1}{2}(w + w\sqrt{1 - 4a^2/w^2}) \quad (w \in \mathbb{C} - [-2a, 2a]).$$

3.7 We know, from Problem 3.6, that $f(z) = J_a^{-1}(z)$ is a one-one conformal mapping from $\mathbb{C} - [-2a, 2a]$ onto $\mathbb{C} - K_a$. Now we show that $f = J_a^{-1}$ satisfies Condition (3.5).

The binomial series for $\left(1 - 4a^2/z^2\right)^{1/2}$ is

$$\left(1 - 4a^2/z^2\right)^{1/2}$$
$$= 1 + \tfrac{1}{2}\left(-4a^2/z^2\right) + \tfrac{1}{2}\left(-\tfrac{1}{2}\right)\frac{\left(-4a^2/z^2\right)^2}{2!} + \cdots,$$
$$\text{for } \left|-4a^2/z^2\right| < 1,$$
$$= 1 - \frac{2a^2}{z^2} - \frac{2a^4}{z^4} - \cdots, \quad \text{for } |z| > 2a.$$

Hence

$$J_a^{-1}(z) = \tfrac{1}{2}\left(z + z\left(1 - \frac{2a^2}{z^2} - \frac{2a^4}{z^4} - \cdots\right)\right)$$
$$= z - \frac{a^2}{z} - \frac{a^4}{z^3} - \cdots, \quad \text{for } |z| > 2a,$$

so that Condition (3.5) is satisfied.

It follows from the Flow Mapping Theorem that the flow velocity function is

$$q(z) = q_{a,c}\left(J_a^{-1}(z)\right)\overline{\left(J_a^{-1}\right)'(z)}$$

$$= \overline{\left(1 - \frac{a^2}{\left(J_a^{-1}(z)\right)^2} - \frac{ic}{J_a^{-1}(z)}\right)}\,\overline{\left(J_a^{-1}\right)'(z)}.$$

By the Inverse Function Rule,

$$\left(J_a^{-1}\right)'(z) = \frac{1}{J_a'\left(J_a^{-1}(z)\right)}$$
$$= \left(1 - a^2/\left(J_a^{-1}(z)\right)^2\right)^{-1}$$
$$\left(\text{since } J_a'(w) = 1 - a^2/w^2\right)$$
$$= \frac{\left(J_a^{-1}(z)\right)^2}{\left(J_a^{-1}(z)\right)^2 - a^2},$$

so that

$$q(z) = \overline{\left(1 - \frac{a^2}{\left(J_a^{-1}(z)\right)^2} - \frac{ic}{J_a^{-1}(z)}\right)\left(\frac{\left(J_a^{-1}(z)\right)^2}{\left(J_a^{-1}(z)\right)^2 - a^2}\right)}$$

$$= 1 - \overline{\left(\frac{ic}{J_a^{-1}(z) - a^2/J_a^{-1}(z)}\right)}$$

$$= 1 - \overline{\left(\frac{ic}{z\sqrt{1 - 4a^2/z^2}}\right)}$$
$$\left(\text{since } J_a^{-1}(z) + a^2/J_a^{-1}(z) = z\right).$$

3.8 (a) The given circle is

$$C_r = \{w : |w| = r\} = \{re^{it} : 0 \le t \le 2\pi\}.$$

The image under J_a of a typical point in C_r is

$$J_a\left(re^{it}\right) = re^{it} + \frac{a^2}{r}e^{-it}$$
$$= \left(r + \frac{a^2}{r}\right)\cos t + i\left(r - \frac{a^2}{r}\right)\sin t.$$

The image set $J_a(C_r)$ is therefore

$$\left\{\left(r + \frac{a^2}{r}\right)\cos t + i\left(r - \frac{a^2}{r}\right)\sin t : 0 \le t \le 2\pi\right\}$$
$$= \left\{x + iy : \frac{x^2}{(r + a^2/r)^2} + \frac{y^2}{(r - a^2/r)^2} = 1\right\}.$$

This is an ellipse in the z-plane, with semi-major axis $r + a^2/r$ and semi-minor axis $r - a^2/r$, as shown in Figure 3.9.

(b) The function J_a^{-1} is a one-one conformal mapping from $\mathbb{C} - [-2a, 2a]$ onto K_a, where $K_a = \{w : |w| \le a\}$. It maps the boundary $\partial K = J_a(C_r)$ of the given obstacle to the boundary $\partial K_r = C_r$ of the disc $K_r = \{w : |w| \le r\}$. Hence the restriction f of J_a^{-1} to $\mathbb{C} - K$ is a one-one conformal mapping from $\mathbb{C} - K$ onto $\mathbb{C} - K_r$.

Also, by Problem 3.7, we know that f satisfies Condition (3.5).

It follows from the Flow Mapping Theorem, and using the Inverse Function Rule as in the solution to Problem 3.7, that the flow velocity function is

$$q(z) = q_{r,c}\left(J_a^{-1}(z)\right)\overline{\left(J_a^{-1}\right)'(z)}$$

$$= \overline{\left(1 - \frac{r^2}{\left(J_a^{-1}(z)\right)^2} - \frac{ic}{J_a^{-1}(z)}\right)}\,\overline{\left(J_a^{-1}\right)'(z)}$$

$$= \overline{\left(\frac{\left(J_a^{-1}(z)\right)^2 - r^2 - icJ_a^{-1}(z)}{\left(J_a^{-1}(z)\right)^2}\right)\left(\frac{\left(J_a^{-1}(z)\right)^2}{\left(J_a^{-1}(z)\right)^2 - a^2}\right)}$$

$$= \overline{\left(\frac{\left(J_a^{-1}(z)\right)^2 - a^2 + a^2 - r^2 - icJ_a^{-1}(z)}{\left(J_a^{-1}(z)\right)^2 - a^2}\right)}$$

$$= 1 - \overline{\left(\frac{r^2 - a^2 + icJ_a^{-1}(z)}{\left(J_a^{-1}(z)\right)^2 - a^2}\right)},$$

where $J_a^{-1}(z) = \tfrac{1}{2}(z + z\sqrt{1 - 4a^2/z^2})$.

3.9 (a) The function J_a^{-1} maps the boundary ∂K of the aerofoil onto C, as well as mapping $\mathbb{C} - K$ one-one onto $\mathbb{C} - D$, where D is the closed disc with boundary C. Furthermore, the translation $g(w) = w + b$ maps C to $\partial K_{(a+b)}$, where $K_{(a+b)} = \{w : |w| \le a + b\}$, as well as mapping $\mathbb{C} - D$ one-one onto $\mathbb{C} - K_{(a+b)}$. Thus the composite function

$$f(z) = \left(g \circ J_a^{-1}\right)(z) = J_a^{-1}(z) + b$$

maps ∂K to $\partial K_{(a+b)}$, and also maps $\mathbb{C} - K$ one-one onto $\mathbb{C} - K_{(a+b)}$.

Since both J_a^{-1} and g satisfy Condition (3.5), so does f. By the Flow Mapping Theorem (with $a + b$ in place of a), a suitable complex potential for the flow described is

$$\Omega(z) = (\Omega_{(a+b),c} \circ f)(z)$$
$$= \Omega_{(a+b),c}\left(J_a^{-1}(z) + b\right)$$
$$= w + b + \frac{(a+b)^2}{w + b} - ic\,\mathrm{Log}(w + b),$$

where

$$w = J_a^{-1}(z) = \tfrac{1}{2}(z + z\sqrt{1 - 4a^2/z^2}).$$

(b) Using the Chain Rule (or directly from the formula given in the theorem), we obtain

$$q(z) = \overline{\left(1 - \frac{(a+b)^2}{(w+b)^2} - \frac{ic}{w+b}\right)\left(J_a^{-1}\right)'(z)}$$

where, as in Problem 3.7,

$$\left(J_a^{-1}\right)'(z) = \left(1 - \frac{a^2}{\left(J_a^{-1}(z)\right)^2}\right)^{-1} = \left(1 - \frac{a^2}{w^2}\right)^{-1}.$$

It follows that, in terms of $w = J_a^{-1}(z)$, the flow velocity function is

$$q(z) = \overline{\frac{w^2}{w^2 - a^2}\left(1 - \frac{(a+b)^2}{(w+b)^2} - \frac{ic}{w+b}\right)}.$$

Now as $z \to 2a$, we have $w = J_a^{-1}(z) \to a$. Also

$$q(z) = \overline{\frac{w^2}{w^2 - a^2}\left(\frac{(w+a+2b)(w-a)}{(w+b)^2} - \frac{ic}{w+b}\right)}$$

$$= \overline{\left(\frac{w^2(w+a+2b)}{(w+a)(w+b)^2} - \frac{icw^2}{(w+b)(w^2-a^2)}\right)}.$$

Thus if $c \neq 0$, then $\lim_{z \to 2a} q(z)$ does not exist. If $c = 0$, then the limiting velocity as $z \to 2a$ is $a/(a+b)$.

3.10 **(a)** From Equation (3.10), since $\alpha = ae^{-i\phi}$ and $a > 0$, we have

$$J_\alpha = R_\phi^{-1} \circ J_a \circ R_\phi.$$

If B is the circle $R_\phi^{-1}(C)$, then

$$C = R_\phi(B).$$

It follows that

$$\partial K = \left(R_\phi^{-1} \circ J_a\right)(C)$$
$$= \left(R_\phi^{-1} \circ J_a \circ R_\phi\right)(B)$$
$$= J_\alpha(B).$$

(b) Let D be the closed disc with boundary B which has centre $-be^{-i\phi}$ and radius $a + b$. The function J_α^{-1} maps $\mathbb{C} - K$ onto $\mathbb{C} - D$, and the translation $g(w) = w + be^{-i\phi}$ maps $\mathbb{C} - D$ onto $\mathbb{C} - K_{(a+b)}$.

The restriction f of the function

$$\left(g \circ J_\alpha^{-1}\right)(z) = J_\alpha^{-1}(z) + be^{-i\phi}$$

to $\mathbb{C} - K$ is a one-one conformal mapping from $\mathbb{C} - K$ onto $\mathbb{C} - K_{(a+b)}$.

Also, f satisfies Condition (3.5) since g and J_α^{-1} do.

Hence, by the Flow Mapping Theorem, a suitable complex potential for flow past K, with circulation $2\pi c$ around K, is given by

$$\Omega(z) = (\Omega_{(a+b),c} \circ f)(z)$$
$$= \Omega_{(a+b),c}\left(J_\alpha^{-1}(z) + be^{-i\phi}\right)$$
$$= w + be^{-i\phi} + \frac{(a+b)^2}{w + be^{-i\phi}} - ic\,\text{Log}\left(w + be^{-i\phi}\right),$$

where $w = J_\alpha^{-1}(z)$.

(c) The method of Problem 3.7 can be used to show that

$$\left(J_\alpha^{-1}\right)'(z) = \left(1 - \frac{\alpha^2}{w^2}\right)^{-1} = \frac{w^2}{w^2 - \alpha^2}.$$

Following the hint, we use the variables

$$w_1 = w - \alpha = w - ae^{-i\phi},$$
$$w_2 = w + be^{-i\phi} = w_1 + (a+b)e^{-i\phi}.$$

We may then write, by the Flow Mapping Theorem,

$$\overline{q}(z) = \left(1 - \frac{(a+b)^2}{w_2^2} - \frac{ic}{w_2}\right)\frac{w^2}{w_1(w+\alpha)}$$

$$= \frac{w^2\left(w_2^2 - (a+b)^2 - icw_2\right)}{w_1(w+\alpha)w_2^2}$$

$$= \frac{w^2\left(w_1^2 + Pw_1 + Q\right)}{w_1(w+\alpha)w_2^2},$$

where

$$P = 2(a+b)e^{-i\phi} - ic,$$
$$Q = (a+b)\left((a+b)\left(e^{-2i\phi} - 1\right) - ice^{-i\phi}\right).$$

Now the limit

$$\lim_{z \to 2\alpha} q(z) = \lim_{w \to \alpha} q(z) = \lim_{w_1 \to 0} q(z)$$

exists if and only if $Q = 0$, that is, if and only if

$$c = \frac{(a+b)\left(e^{-2i\phi} - 1\right)}{ie^{-i\phi}}$$
$$= -i(a+b)\left(e^{-i\phi} - e^{i\phi}\right)$$
$$= -2(a+b)\sin\phi.$$

(For this value of c, we have

$$\lim_{z \to 2\alpha} \overline{q}(z) = \frac{\alpha^2 P}{2\alpha(a+b)^2 e^{-2i\phi}}$$

$$= \frac{ae^{i\phi}\left(2(a+b)e^{-i\phi} + 2i(a+b)\sin\phi\right)}{2(a+b)^2}$$

$$= \frac{ae^{i\phi}\cos\phi}{a+b}.$$

The complex conjugate of this is

$$\lim_{z \to 2\alpha} q(z) = \frac{ae^{-i\phi}\cos\phi}{a+b} = \frac{\alpha\cos\phi}{a+b}.$$

As $\phi \to 0$, this expression tends to the value $a/(a+b)$ found in the solution to Problem 3.9.)

Section 4

4.1 If the ball is pushed sideways from the centre of the airstream, then the flow speed on the side of the ball closest to the stream centre will be greater than that on the opposite side, since the latter part of the flow encounters more resistance to its motion due to the ball. Bernoulli's Equation predicts that there is, in consequence, a higher pressure on the side further from the stream centre, and the pressure difference provides a force (from the higher pressure region to the lower) which tends to restore the ball to its central position in the airstream.

4.2 **(a)** By applying Bernoulli's Equation,

$$p(z) + \tfrac{1}{2}\rho|q(z)|^2 = p_0,$$

to the velocity function

$$q_{a,c}(z) = \overline{1 - \frac{a^2}{z^2} - \frac{ic}{z}},$$

we obtain

$$p(z) = p_0 - \frac{\rho}{2}\left(1 - \frac{a^2}{z^2} - \frac{ic}{z}\right)\left(1 - \frac{a^2}{\overline{z}^2} + \frac{ic}{\overline{z}}\right).$$

(b) On putting $z = ae^{it}$ and $\overline{z} = ae^{-it}$ into the expression for $p(z)$ in part (a), we find that

$$p(ae^{it}) = p_0 - \frac{\rho}{2}\left(1 - e^{-2it} - \frac{ice^{-it}}{a}\right)\left(1 - e^{2it} + \frac{ice^{it}}{a}\right)$$

$$= p_0 - \frac{\rho}{2}\left(e^{it} - e^{-it} - \frac{ic}{a}\right)\left(e^{-it} - e^{it} + \frac{ic}{a}\right)$$

$$= p_0 + \frac{\rho}{2}\left(e^{it} - e^{-it} - \frac{ic}{a}\right)^2$$

$$= p_0 + \frac{\rho}{2}\left(2i\sin t - \frac{ic}{a}\right)^2$$

$$= p_0 - \frac{\rho}{2}\left(2\sin t - \frac{c}{a}\right)^2.$$

(c) The symmetry of $p(ae^{it})$ about the imaginary axis follows from the fact that

$$\sin t = \sin(\pi - t).$$

If $c = 0$, then there is symmetry of $p(ae^{it})$ also about the real axis, because

$$\sin t = -\sin(-t),$$

so that

$$\sin^2 t = \sin^2(-t).$$

(These symmetry results also apply to the flow as a whole. We have

$$p(z) = p(\bar{z}),$$

for symmetry about the real axis, when $c = 0$, and

$$p(z) = p(-\bar{z}),$$

for symmetry about the imaginary axis.)

4.3 The required total force is

$$F = -a \int_0^{2\pi} \left(p_0 - \frac{\rho}{2}\left(2\sin t - \frac{c}{a} \right)^2 \right) e^{it} dt.$$

Now we have

$$-a \int_0^{2\pi} \left(p_0 - \frac{\rho c^2}{2a^2} \right) e^{it} dt = 0,$$

so the real part of F is

$$\operatorname{Re} F = 2\rho \int_0^{2\pi} \left(a\sin^2 t - c\sin t \right)\cos t\, dt$$

$$= 2\rho\left[\tfrac{1}{3}a\sin^3 t - \tfrac{1}{2}c\sin^2 t \right]_0^{2\pi}$$

$$= 0,$$

and the imaginary part of F is

$$\operatorname{Im} F = 2\rho \int_0^{2\pi} \left(a\sin^3 t - c\sin^2 t \right) dt$$

$$= 2\rho \int_0^{2\pi} \left(a\left(1 - \cos^2 t\right)\sin t - \tfrac{1}{2}c(1 - \cos 2t) \right) dt$$

$$= 2\rho\left[-a\left(\cos t - \tfrac{1}{3}\cos^3 t\right) - \tfrac{1}{2}c\left(t - \tfrac{1}{2}\sin 2t\right) \right]_0^{2\pi}$$

$$= -2\pi\rho c.$$

Hence we have $F = -2\pi\rho ci$. The lift is $-2\pi\rho c$ (positive if $c < 0$), and the drag is zero.

4.4 Applying Blasius' Theorem, the conjugate force is

$$\overline{F} = \tfrac{1}{2}i\rho \int_{\partial K} \left(1 - \frac{a^2}{z^2} - \frac{ic}{z} \right)^2 dz$$

$$= \tfrac{1}{2}i\rho \int_{\partial K} \left(1 - \frac{2ic}{z} - \frac{2a^2 + c^2}{z^2} + \frac{2ia^2 c}{z^3} + \frac{a^4}{z^4} \right) dz$$

$$= 2\pi\rho ci \quad \text{(by the Residue Theorem).}$$

The total force on the cylinder is therefore $F = -2\pi\rho ci$ (per unit length into the page).

4.5 The lift is given by the Kutta–Joukowski Lift Theorem as $-2\pi c\rho$. Also, from Problem 3.10(c), the Kutta–Joukowski Hypothesis holds if and only if

$$c = -2(a + b)\sin\phi.$$

In this case, the lift on the aerofoil is

$$-2\pi\rho(-2(a + b)\sin\phi) = 4\pi\rho(a + b)\sin\phi.$$

This lift is positive for $0 < \phi < \pi$, and increases with ϕ for $0 < \phi \le \pi/2$.

In practice, this prediction for the lift is borne out only for small values of the angle of attack ϕ. Above $15°$ or so, there is a rapid decrease in the lift provided (stalling), and flight can no longer be sustained.

SOLUTIONS TO THE EXERCISES

Section 1

1.1 **(a)** From Equation (1.1), with $q(z) = 3e^{7i\pi/12}$ and $\theta = -2\pi/3$, we have

$$q_{-2\pi/3}(z) = \text{Re}\big(3e^{-7i\pi/12}e^{-2i\pi/3}\big)$$
$$= \text{Re}\big(3e^{-5i\pi/4}\big)$$
$$= 3\cos\left(-\frac{5\pi}{4}\right)$$
$$= -3/\sqrt{2}.$$

(b) The second direction is specified by

$$-ie^{-2i\pi/3} = e^{-i\pi/2}e^{-2i\pi/3} = e^{-7i\pi/6} = e^{5i\pi/6},$$

so that the required component is

$$q_{5\pi/6}(z) = \text{Re}\big(3e^{-7i\pi/12}e^{5i\pi/6}\big)$$
$$= \text{Re}\big(3e^{i\pi/4}\big)$$
$$= 3\cos\frac{\pi}{4}$$
$$= 3/\sqrt{2}.$$

1.2 We have

$$\bar{q}(z)e^{i\theta} = \text{Re}\big(\bar{q}(z)e^{i\theta}\big) + i\,\text{Im}\big(\bar{q}(z)e^{i\theta}\big)$$
$$= q_\theta(z) + iq_{(\theta-\pi/2)}(z) \quad \text{(by Equations (1.2)).}$$

Taking the complex conjugate of both sides, we obtain

$$q(z)e^{-i\theta} = q_\theta(z) - iq_{(\theta-\pi/2)}(z),$$

so that

$$q(z) = (q_\theta(z) - iq_{(\theta-\pi/2)}(z))e^{i\theta}.$$

1.3 **(a)** The conjugate velocity function is

$$\bar{q}(z) = 1 - \frac{1}{z^2},$$

so that, from Equation (1.7), we obtain

$$\mathcal{C}_\Gamma + i\mathcal{F}_\Gamma = \int_\Gamma \left(1 - \frac{1}{z^2}\right)dz.$$

This integral can be shown to be zero either by using the standard parametrization for the contour Γ, or by applying the Residue Theorem. Hence we have

$$\mathcal{C}_\Gamma = \mathcal{F}_\Gamma = 0.$$

(b) (i) The conjugate velocity function $\bar{q}$ is analytic on $\mathbb{C} - \{0\}$. Hence, by Theorem 1.2, q is a model flow velocity function on this region.

(ii) The real and imaginary parts of

$$q(z) = 1 - \frac{1}{\bar{z}^2} = 1 - \frac{z^2}{|z|^4} = 1 - \frac{(x+iy)^2}{(x^2+y^2)^2}$$

are, respectively,

$$q_1(x,y) = 1 - \frac{x^2-y^2}{(x^2+y^2)^2}, \quad q_2(x,y) = -\frac{2xy}{(x^2+y^2)^2}.$$

The partial derivatives of q_1 and q_2 are

$$\frac{\partial q_1}{\partial x} = \frac{2x(x^2-3y^2)}{(x^2+y^2)^3}, \quad \frac{\partial q_1}{\partial y} = \frac{2y(3x^2-y^2)}{(x^2+y^2)^3},$$

$$\frac{\partial q_2}{\partial x} = \frac{2y(3x^2-y^2)}{(x^2+y^2)^3}, \quad \frac{\partial q_2}{\partial y} = \frac{2x(3y^2-x^2)}{(x^2+y^2)^3}.$$

Hence we find, if $z \neq 0$, that

$$\frac{\partial q_1}{\partial x} + \frac{\partial q_2}{\partial y} = 0 \quad \text{and} \quad \frac{\partial q_2}{\partial x} - \frac{\partial q_1}{\partial y} = 0.$$

By Theorem 1.3, q is locally both flux-free and circulation-free; that is, q is a model flow velocity function.

Section 2

2.1 **(a)** The sketch below was obtained by considering the flow expected when a source is placed in a uniform flow. (It may be confirmed by using the stream function derived in part (b).)

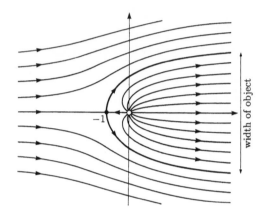

The source of strength 4π at the origin has flow velocity function $2/\bar{z}$, so that the overall velocity function here is

$$q(z) = 2\left(1 + \frac{1}{\bar{z}}\right).$$

The stagnation point is the solution of the equation $q(z) = 0$, which is $z = -1$.

(b) A complex potential for this flow is

$$\Omega(z) = 2(z + \text{Log}\,z) \quad (z \in \mathbb{C}_\pi),$$

and so the corresponding stream function is

$$\text{Im}\,\Omega(z) = 2(\text{Im}\,z + \text{Arg}\,z).$$

The stagnation point at $z = -1$ lies outside the domain of Ω, but we have

$$\lim_{z \to -1}(\text{Im}\,z) = 0 \quad \text{and} \quad \lim_{z \to -1}(\text{Arg}\,z) = \pm\pi,$$

where the plus or minus sign is chosen depending on whether the limit is taken from above or below the real axis, respectively. Hence the curved streamlines which emerge from the stagnation point have equations

$$y + \text{Arg}\,z = \pm\pi.$$

The width of the object outlined by these streamlines, corresponding to the point $z = x + iy$ on the upper streamline, is

$$2y = 2(\pi - \text{Arg}\,z).$$

The maximum width (never attained, but equal to the limiting width as $z \to \infty$ along the streamline and hence $\text{Arg}\,z \to 0$) is therefore 2π.

2.2 If q is a model flow velocity function which has domain $\mathbb{C}$ and is bounded, then there exists a real number K such that

$$|q(z)| \leq K, \quad \text{for } z \in \mathbb{C}.$$

But $\bar{q}$ is an analytic function with the same domain as q, and is therefore entire. Also, we have

$$|\bar{q}(z)| = |q(z)|, \quad \text{for } z \in \mathbb{C},$$

so that $\bar{q}$ is also bounded. It follows from Liouville's Theorem that $\bar{q}$ is a constant function, and hence that q is constant. The corresponding flow is therefore uniform.

Section 3

3.1 The stream function is

$$\operatorname{Im} \Omega(z) = y\left(1 - \frac{a^2}{x^2 + y^2}\right),$$

which is constant on each streamline. Thus the streamline through $2ai$ (at which point, $x = 0$ and $y = 2a$) has the equation

$$y\left(1 - \frac{a^2}{x^2 + y^2}\right) = 2a\left(1 - \frac{a^2}{4a^2}\right) = \tfrac{3}{2}a.$$

As $z \to \infty$, we have $\left(x^2 + y^2\right)^{-1} \to 0$. Hence $y \to \tfrac{3}{2}a$, and so the distance between the streamline through $2ai$ and the real axis tends towards the limiting value $\tfrac{3}{2}a$.

3.2 (a) The Joukowski function J is a one-one conformal mapping from $\mathbb{C} - K_1$ onto $\mathbb{C} - [-2, 2]$. Also, we have

$$J([1,2]) = \left\{z + \frac{1}{z} : z \in \mathbb{R}, 1 \leq z \leq 2\right\} = \left[2, \tfrac{5}{2}\right],$$

and, similarly,

$$J([-2,-1]) = \left[-\tfrac{5}{2}, -2\right].$$

The required result follows.

(b) The image under J_a of $\mathbb{C} - K_a$ is $\mathbb{C} - [-2a, 2a]$, so we choose $a = \tfrac{5}{4}$.

(c) The function $f = J_{5/4}^{-1} \circ J$ is a one-one conformal mapping from $\mathbb{C} - K$ onto $\mathbb{C} - K_{5/4}$, which satisfies Condition (3.5), by the hint.

Hence, by the Flow Mapping Theorem, a complex potential function for this Obstacle Problem is

$$\begin{aligned}
\Omega(z) &= (\Omega_{5/4,c} \circ f)(z) \\
&= J(z) - ic \operatorname{Log}\left(J_{5/4}^{-1}(J(z))\right),
\end{aligned}$$

by the hint.

Proceeding as in the solution to Problem 3.5, with $a = 5/4$ rather than 1 and $J(z)$ in place of z, we find that the velocity function is

$$q(z) = \overline{\left(1 - \frac{ic}{J(z)\sqrt{1 - 25/(2J(z))^2}}\right)} J'(z).$$

3.3 The boundary ellipse here is of the same form as that considered in Problem 3.8, but rotated through an angle $\pi/2$. Hence the function

$$R_{-\pi/2}^{-1} \circ J_a \circ R_{-\pi/2} = J_\alpha,$$

where $\alpha = ae^{i\pi/2} = ai$, is a one-one conformal mapping from $\mathbb{C} - K_r$ onto $\mathbb{C} - K$, where $K_r = \{w : |w| \leq r\}$.

It follows that the function $f = J_{ai}^{-1}$ is a one-one conformal mapping from $\mathbb{C} - K$ onto $\mathbb{C} - K_r$. Also, as in the solution to Problem 3.7, $f = J_{ai}^{-1}$ satisfies Condition (3.5).

Hence, by the Flow Mapping Theorem, a complex potential function for this Obstacle Problem is

$$\begin{aligned}
\Omega(z) &= \left(\Omega_{r,c} \circ J_{ai}^{-1}\right)(z) \\
&= z + \frac{r^2 + a^2}{J_{ai}^{-1}(z)} - ic \operatorname{Log}\left(J_{ai}^{-1}(z)\right),
\end{aligned}$$

where

$$J_{ai}^{-1}(z) = \tfrac{1}{2}(z + z\sqrt{1 + 4a^2/z^2}).$$

Proceeding as in the solution to Problem 3.8, we find that the flow velocity function is

$$\begin{aligned}
q(z) &= \overline{\left(1 - \frac{r^2}{(f(z))^2} - \frac{ic}{f(z)}\right) f'(z)} \\
&= 1 - \overline{\left(\frac{r^2 + a^2 + icJ_{ai}^{-1}(z)}{\left(J_{ai}^{-1}(z)\right)^2 + a^2}\right)}.
\end{aligned}$$

Section 4

4.1 On taking the conjugate of the expression for $q(z)$, and squaring, we have

$$\begin{aligned}
(\bar{q}(z))^2 &= 1 - \frac{2ic}{z\sqrt{1 - 4a^2/z^2}} - \frac{c^2}{z^2 - 4a^2} \\
&= 2\bar{q}(z) - 1 - \frac{c^2}{z^2 - 4a^2}.
\end{aligned}$$

By applying Equation (4.4) and using the hint, we obtain

$$\begin{aligned}
\overline{F} &= \tfrac{1}{2}i\rho \int_\Gamma (\bar{q}(z))^2 \, dz, \\
&= \tfrac{1}{2}i\rho \int_\Gamma \left(2\bar{q}(z) - 1 - \frac{c^2}{z^2 - 4a^2}\right) dz \\
&= \tfrac{1}{2}i\rho \left(4\pi c - \int_\Gamma \frac{c^2}{z^2 - 4a^2} \, dz\right),
\end{aligned}$$

where Γ is any simple-closed contour surrounding K.

The remaining integral can be shown to be zero, by the Residue Theorem (the integrand has simple poles at $\pm 2a$, and the residues at these poles cancel out). Hence $\overline{F} = 2\pi\rho ci$, so that the force on the plate is

$$F = -2\pi\rho ci.$$

4.2 The function J^{-1} maps $\mathbb{C} - K$ onto $\mathbb{C} - D$, and the translation $g(w) = w - \beta$ maps $\mathbb{C} - D$ onto $\mathbb{C} - K_{|1-\beta|}$, where $K_{|1-\beta|}$ is the closed disc with centre 0 and radius $|1 - \beta|$. Hence the function $f = g \circ J^{-1}$ is a one-one conformal mapping from $\mathbb{C} - K$ onto $\mathbb{C} - K_{|1-\beta|}$.

Also, since g and J^{-1} satisfy Condition (3.5), so does $f = g \circ J^{-1}$.

Hence, by the Flow Mapping Theorem, a complex potential function for this Obstacle Problem is

$$\begin{aligned}
\Omega(z) &= (\Omega_{|1-\beta|,c} \circ f)(z) \\
&= \Omega_{|1-\beta|,c}\left(J^{-1}(z) - \beta\right) \\
&= w - \beta + \frac{|1-\beta|^2}{w - \beta} - ic \operatorname{Log}(w - \beta),
\end{aligned}$$

where $w = J^{-1}(z)$.

The corresponding conjugate velocity function is

$$\bar{q}(z) = \left(1 - \frac{|1-\beta|^2}{(w-\beta)^2} - \frac{ic}{w-\beta}\right) \frac{w^2}{w^2-1},$$

since $\left(J^{-1}\right)'(z) = w^2/\left(w^2-1\right)$; see the solution to Problem 3.7, with $a = 1$.

This tends to ∞ as $z \to 2$ (corresponding to $w \to 1$) unless

$$\lim_{w \to 1} \left(1 - \frac{|1-\beta|^2}{(w-\beta)^2} - \frac{ic}{w-\beta}\right) = 0;$$

that is, unless

$$c = -i\left(1 - \beta - \frac{|1-\beta|^2}{1-\beta}\right)$$

$$= -i(1 - \beta - \overline{(1-\beta)})$$

$$= i(\beta - \bar{\beta})$$

$$= -2\operatorname{Im}\beta.$$

This is the value which c must take, according to the Kutta–Joukowski Hypothesis. By the Kutta–Joukowski Lift Theorem, the corresponding force on K is then

$$F = -2\pi c\rho i = 4\pi\rho i\operatorname{Im}\beta.$$